M000279432

# EINSTEIN,
# GERTRUDE STEIN,
# WITTGENSTEIN
# &
# FRANKENSTEIN

**ALSO BY JOHN BROCKMAN**


By the Late John Brockman

37

Afterwords

Real Time 1
*(with Edward Rosenfeld)*

Real Time 2
*(with Edward Rosenfeld)*

About Bateson

The Philosopher's Game
*(with Edwin Schlossberg)*

# EINSTEIN, GERTRUDE STEIN, WITTGENSTEIN & FRANKENSTEIN

---

## *Re-Inventing the Universe*

---

### JOHN BROCKMAN

**VIKING**

VIKING
Viking Penguin Inc., 40 West 23rd Street,
New York, New York 10010, U.S.A.
Penguin Books Ltd, Harmondsworth, Middlesex, England
Penguin Books Australia Ltd, Ringwood, Victoria, Australia
Penguin Books Canada Limited, 2801 John Street,
Markham, Ontario, Canada L3R 1B4
Penguin Books (N.Z.) Ltd, 182–190 Wairau Road,
Auckland 10, New Zealand

Copyright © John Brockman, 1986
All rights reserved

First published in 1986 by Viking Penguin Inc.
Published simultaneously in Canada

Research Associate: Michael C. Talbot
Illustrator: Matthew Zimet

LIBRARY OF CONGRESS CATALOGING IN PUBLICATION DATA
Brockman, John, 1941–
Einstein, Gertrude Stein, Wittgenstein &
Frankenstein.
Bibliography: p.
1. Science.   2. Cosmology.   I. Title.   II. Title:
Einstein, Gertrude Stein, Wittgenstein &
Frankenstein.
Q158.5.B76   1986      500      85-40568
ISBN 0-670-80480-0

Page 307 constitutes an extension of this copyright page.

Printed in the United States of America by
R. R. Donnelley & Sons Company, Harrisonburg, Virginia
Set in Granjon

Without limiting the rights under copyright reserved above, no part of this
publication may be reproduced, stored in or introduced into a retrieval
system, or transmitted, in any form or by any means (electronic, mechanical, photocopying, recording or otherwise), without the prior written permission of both the copyright owner and the above publisher of this book.

In memory of my father,
Ellis Brockman
(1911–1985)

# *Acknowledgments*

A book such as this could not have been written without a great deal of help. I am very grateful to the scientists who took the time to talk to me about their work. They include Philip Brockman, David Bohm, Sidney Coleman, Paul Davies, Gerald Feinberg, Edward Feigenbaum, Alan Guth, John Lilly, Lynn Margulis, Richard Muller, Heinz Pagels, Roger Schank, Jacob Shahem, Robert Shapiro, David Shaw, Rupert Sheldrake, Joseph Traub, Roy Walford, and Frank Wilczek. Other scientists, including Daniel Hillis and Stephen Wolfram, were kind enough to supply me with research papers and related materials. A number of the above read sections of the manuscript and offered useful suggestions and criticisms. In particular, I wish to thank Gerald Feinberg, Heinz Pagels, and my brother Philip Brockman for their detailed comments.

A number of friends and colleagues have also read either part or all of the manuscript and offered comments. They include Richard Baker, Stewart Brand, Arthur Dubow, Joseph Esposito, Michael Katz, Steven Levy, Pamela McCorduck, Richard Morris, Richard Rabkin, Joan Richardson, Paul Ryan, Toby Sanders, Edwin Schlossberg, David Warsh, Jeffrey Weiss, Camilo Wilson, and Kim Witherspoon.

I wish to thank Michael Talbot, my research associate, for his valuable contribution, and Matthew Zimet for his line drawings. Daniel Frank, my editor, offered helpful suggestions, and Katinka Matson, my agent, was there when I needed her.

# Contents

# INTRODUCTION

# *Einstein, Gertrude Stein, Wittgenstein & Frankenstein*

Man creates tools and then molds himself in their image. Reality is manmade. The universe is an invention, a metaphor.

*The heart is a pump* is a statement we all accept as a truism. *The brain is a computer* is a statement that many have now begun to accept. Isaac Newton created a mechanistic methodology and we invented ourselves in terms of mechanistic language. Newton's methodology influenced the reductionist view that led the medical establishment to look at hearts, lungs, and livers—in short, to understand the human body primarily in terms of its respective parts. Now, as a result of computer technology, a doctor takes a blood sample, runs it through a computer, and receives a cryptic readout of hundreds of pieces of diagnostic information. Instead of machines, we view ourselves as an information process. The metaphor continually changes.

Whatever descriptive language we have arrived at to understand reality *becomes* the reality. We don't say the heart is *like* a pump. The heart *is* a pump.

The notion that reality is nothing more than the immaterial and transient web of our descriptive language has been arrived at in various ways by a number of important thinkers. One of the most prominent of these was the German physicist Werner Heisenberg, who, in his now well-known uncertainty principle, demonstrated that at its most fundamental or subatomic level, reality is not so much "observed" as it is "created" by the physicist. Similarly, the

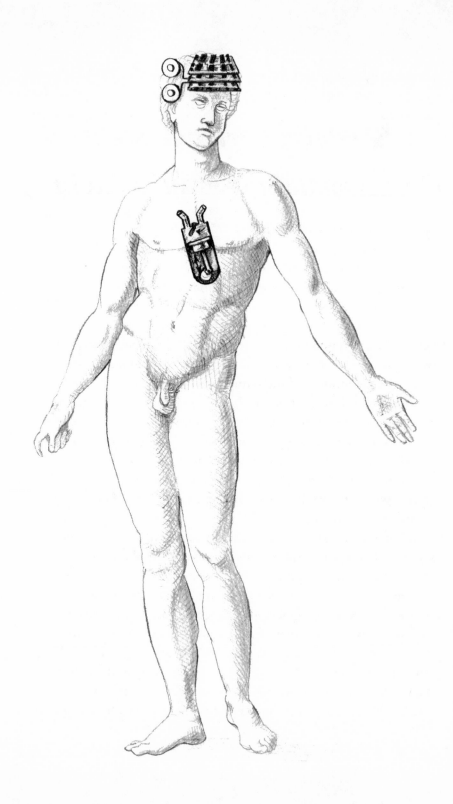

linguist Benjamin Lee Whorf pointed out that no individual can give an absolutely impartial description of reality above and beyond the constraints of his or her language. The poet Wallace Stevens wrote extensively about the primacy of the theory of description. In this regard he considered the world itself to be at once the supreme fiction and the only thing worth thinking about. He wrote that "the final belief is to believe in a fiction, which you know to be a fiction, there being nothing else. The exquisite truth is to know it is a fiction and that you believe in it willingly."[1] Drawing on the work of Stevens, Whorf, and Heisenberg, as well as other thinkers, I wrote a trilogy of books in the late 1960s and early 1970s—By the Late John Brockman, 37, and Afterwords—presenting my belief that the universe is not something we discover but something we invent.

Having concluded that when we offer descriptions of the universe we are not so much exploring reality as creating it, I became less interested in writing about what the universe meant and more interested in seeking out those individuals responsible for the current state of the universe as invention. In 1973 I attended a conference in Big Sur, California, known as the AUM Conference. The purpose of the conference was to spend ten days exploring the work of the British mathematician G. Spencer Brown. In addition to Brown, other participants included philosopher Alan Watts, anthropologist Gregory Bateson, neurophysiologist Karl Pribram, dolphin scientist John Lilly, psychologist Will Schutz, Whole Earth Catalog's Stewart Brand, and cyberneticist and computer logician Heinz Von Foerster.

Each participant was required to give a short talk on his work. This was slightly unnerving to me as I was not a scientist and even lacked a professional reputation others lay claim to. My late invitation had been proffered only after physicist Richard Feynman had

Although people are at ease with the concept of the heart as a pump, the concept of the brain as a computer is just beginning to take hold.

declined to attend. I decided that a low profile was the best policy. I successfully avoided the podium for days, and then early one morning while I was groggily drinking my first cup of coffee, my view of the Pacific Ocean was suddenly eclipsed. Alan Watts and John Lilly, both appropriately dressed in inquisitorial hoods and robes, loomed over me, ordering me to speak that evening.

I had no choice. I knew that I would address the general idea of the universe as invention, the ultimate fiction. As an approach I decided to employ a conceptual framework suggested to me a year or so earlier by my friend, conceptual artist James Lee Byars. During the course of many frequent and intense dialogues Byars laid out his notion of the importance of "the Steins" as a cornerstone of post-modern consciousness. "The Steins," to Byars, included the physicist Albert Einstein, the writer Gertrude Stein, and the philosopher Ludwig Wittgenstein. I believed that in order to confirm the argument of the universe as invention it was also necessary to include the work of cyberneticist Norbert Wiener. As cybernetics has led to the development of artificial intelligence, Dr. Frankenstein—certainly the inventor of the first artificial intelligence— was inserted to represent cybernetic ideas (what good are theories without style?). In the talk each Stein symbolized the following:

Einstein represented the revolution in physics of the twentieth century culminating in a universe in which reality is theory, where space and time do not exist except as relative to the observer, where all the pictures of nature are mathematical pictures, where there is an ultimate boundary of physical knowledge in the form of media through which we perceive it. The idea of the curvature of space, a space that cannot be directly experienced by our senses, is perhaps the most obvious instance in which the universe ceases to be something that is perceived and is most clearly a mental act. The universe isn't there. It simply is.

In *The First Reader* Gertrude Stein wrote about how Johnny measured Jimmy and how Jimmy measured Johnny until the characters became meaningless and what remained was the act of measurement. She was the first writer who made integral to her work the idea of an indeterminate and discontinuous universe. Words represented neither character nor activity: they were "not imitations either of sounds or colors or emotions." Language was an intellectual re-creation. Through an emphasis on such stylistic devices as repetition she used language to deny meaning and representational concerns. As she pointed out, she would "write as if every instant of writing were complete in itself, as if the fact of writing something were continually becoming true and completing itself, not as if were leading to something." A rose is a rose is a rose. And a universe is a universe is a universe.

Ludwig Wittgenstein wrote, "A picture held us captive. And we could not get outside it, for it lay in our language, and language seemed to repeat it to us inexorably." Wittgenstein's universe is to be found in the limits of language: "The limits of my language mean the limits of my world." In a universe bounded by language there is the tension created by the fact that "what expresses *itself* in language, *we* cannot express by means of language." In reaching this edge of meaning Wittgenstein noted that "what we cannot speak about we must pass over in silence." He believed in a philosophical self that was "not the human being, not the human body, or the human soul, with which psychology deals, but rather the metaphysical subject, the limits of the world—not part of it." In Wittgenstein's philosophical framework, "It is not *how* things are in the world that is mystical, but *that* it exists."

Norbert Wiener's cybernetic theories expanded our understanding of self-organizing systems, be they machines, ideas, ecological systems, or human relationships. Weiner's universe is one that interacts infinitely with itself. If Newtonian physics taught us that it is the parts that matter, Wiener demonstrated the importance of the patterns that connect the parts. Weiner laid the groundwork for the coming artificial-intelligence revolution. As a result, we are about to create the first extension of ourselves in much the same way as Mary Shelley's Dr. Frankenstein pieced together his creation. In a broader context, scientific theories have always been Frankenstein monsters of sorts, often pieced together out of anything scientists may be thinking of at the time. Scientists construct theories based on other theories, some of them wrong, and often with ideas so speculative that the scientists have no idea what they are creating. Again, man creates tools and then molds himself in their image.

After my formal presentation, I asked the various participants to step up to the blackboard behind the podium and write in chalk a succinct one-sentence summary of their view of reality. As each did so, one by one, I followed just inches behind his hand with my eraser, wiping away his words as quickly as they were written.

My talk and the demonstration that meant that "all begins and ends with words" had an unexpected consequence. Many of the attendees at the conference, although fascinating thinkers and writers, did not have literary representation. As I lived in New York and had developed a certain amount of contact and influence with New York publishers, I was again cornered, this time by Lilly and Gregory Bateson and quite literally conscripted into becoming their literary agent. Given my conviction that words were the only reality, what better next step for me to take than to begin selling them? Thus, as a result of my talk at Big Sur that evening, I not only unexpectedly became a literary agent but also began to lay the foundations for this book.

A decade later, I run a literary agency that specializes in representing serious thinkers, helping them to translate their ideas into books. Among our clients are several dozen of the more prominent scientists in the world. A few of the people whose work I cover are clients. Most are not.

In this book I present a status report and appraisal of the most recent and important scientific hypotheses and advances. The selections in the book are idiosyncratic. Rather than being exhaustive I have instead chosen those developments and ideas that are of interest to me personally and that, in my opinion, lend themselves most to human imaging. I have also included a section of highly unorthodox and scientifically unproven ideas which, although on the fringe, are interesting as scientific heresies.

Although my overall thesis is that the universe is an invention and that scientists are creating, not discovering, the world, I have let the scientific ideas presented herein stand by themselves. They are offered in the context of what Wallace Stevens termed "the exquisite environment of fact." As he wrote, "The final poem will be the poem of fact in the language of fact. But it will be the poem of fact not realized before."[2]

In today's world, scientific advances are taking place at a rate unparalleled at any other time in history. The very nature of change itself has evolved so quickly that a hallmark of the twentieth century is the uncertainty with which we all live. This is why I believe the ideas and information included in this book to be essential to anyone interested in knowing who we are, and where we are headed. If there is any lingering doubt that our current understanding of the universe is an invention of our own making, it is quelled by the pace with which the metaphors of science continue to change. For just as Newtonian models of the body are becoming obsolete and cybernetic models based on computer readouts are in their ascendancy, in this book you will find that the universe and all of the things that we know in it are being radically altered and transformed again. This is a book about re-inventing the universe, and, in the words of Rimbaud, it fixes "frenzies in their flight."

# Part I

## THE COSMOLOGICAL UNIVERSE

Every age has invented its own universe. The Greek astronomer Eudoxus believed that the heavens were composed of twenty-seven invisible spheres, with the Earth at their center. Copernicus shattered the spheres and placed the Earth in orbit around the Sun. Newton defined the laws that governed the movement of the planets through space, and with his theory of relativity, Einstein changed the universe again. Instead of space being "nothing," an empty stage through which the Earth moved unimpeded, Einstein revealed that space is "something," that it is curved and itself is one of the actors in the drama of physics.

Even Einstein himself recognized that all such pictures of the universe are "fictitious," or free inventions of the human mind. As he stated, "The fictitious character of the principles is made quite obvious by the fact that it is possible to exhibit two essentially different bases, each of which in its consequences leads to a large measure of agreement with experience."[1] For example, Newton's view that the planets move around the Sun in neat elliptical orbits is borne out accurately in experiments, as is Einstein's theory of relativity, in spite of the fact that both are based on completely different geometrical understandings of space.

Einstein believed that the fact that a variety of different pictures of the universe can be made to fit observation and experience has a drawback in that it has the potential to prevent those who believe in it from arriving at further and more profound understandings.

Indeed, he felt that it was the remarkable success of Newton's theories that kept the eighteenth and nineteenth centuries from discovering the theory of relativity.

However, Einstein also recognized that science could not advance without free invention. As he stated, "We now know that science cannot grow out of empiricism alone, that in the constructions of science we need to use free invention which only *a posteriori* can be confronted with experience as to its usefulness. This fact could elude earlier generations, to whom theoretical creation seemed to grow inductively out of empiricism without the creative influence of a free construction of concepts."[2] Because of this, Einstein concluded that the more a culture recognizes that its current picture of the universe is an invention, the more advanced the status of its science.

In this section we will explore the current state of the universe as invention on its most cosmological scale. As we will find, the process of free invention in science has traced back the origin of the universe to an unprecedented degree. It has proposed the existence of interstellar objects and phenomena more exotic and bizarre than ever before pondered, and it has tackled some of the most profound cosmological questions of all time: How old is the universe? How large is it? Did the universe have a beginning, and will it have an end?

# The Inflationary Scenario

In the 1940s physicists George Gamow, Ralph Alpher, and Robert Herman first proposed the *big-bang* theory of the origin of the universe, and in the years since its inception, it has been accepted by a growing consensus of scientists. About five years ago the first serious attempts were made to describe the universe during the first fractions of a second of the big bang. The results posed some grave questions for the theory.

The big-bang model asserts that the universe began about 10 billion years ago as a primordial fireball of extraordinary temperature and density, which exploded and has been expanding and cooling ever since. The first intimation of this view came in the 1920s when astronomer Edwin Hubble's measurement supported the view that the universe was expanding. When astronomers formed a picture of this expansion and imagined it running backward like a movie in reverse, the resulting scenario was of a universe that grows increasingly denser and hotter. When the cosmic movie rolls back to the ultimate degree, the universe is seen as a dense mass. Temperatures become so hot that planets, matter, even the constituents of matter melt into a dense ball in which subatomic particles such as electrons and protons were no longer differentiated. Herman, Gamow, and Alpher tried to show how all of the known elements could have been created by the thermonuclear processes that resulted from the explosion of the fireball.

Many scientists liked the big-bang scenario because it explained

Hubble's discovery that galaxies recede from one another with a velocity proportional to the distance that separated them. In 1965 the notion received an even more powerful endorsement. Alpher and Herman had predicted that as the big-bang fireball expanded and cooled, it would become less brilliant, but its radiation would remain. In 1965, Arno A. Penzias and Robert W. Wilson of the Bell Telephone Laboratories accidentally discovered that the entire universe was permeated by a background of microwave radiation with an effective temperature of about 3 degrees Kelvin. (They first blamed the mysterious static coming over their instruments on a family of pigeons they found nesting in their equipment, but fortunately they removed the pigeons and pursued the matter further.) With the discovery of what seemed to be a relic of the big bang, more and more scientists started giving the theory credence. As Robert Jastrow has noted, "No explanation other than the big bang has ever been found for the fireball radiation."[1]

The cosmic background radiation had the exact distribution of wavelengths expected for the light and heat produced in a great explosion. The big-bang model also successfully predicted why such light gases as helium and hydrogen, and other elements with relatively low atomic weights, are found in abundance in the universe. With such a profusion of evidence, the big-bang picture of the origin of the universe has currently come to be accepted as fact by a majority of scientists.

The theory is not without its problems. The first lies in the amazing uniformity of the microwave radiation permeating the universe. Studies have shown it to be uniform in temperature in all parts of the universe to about one part in $10^4$. However, in the standard big-bang model, the universe evolves too quickly to allow such a uniformity to have occurred. The fact that it does occur and cannot be accounted for by the standard big-bang theory is known as the *horizon problem*.

Another problem of the standard big-bang picture, one that is really just a restatement of the horizon problem, is that it does not explain the degree of nonuniformity in the universe. Why isn't the universe more homogeneous instead of composed of irregular clumps of matter—galaxies and clusters of galaxies—interspersed with vast tracts of open space? In the standard big-bang model it can't be assumed that this lack of homogeneity has existed from the very beginning. There is no problem with this nonuniformity over the past several billion years. However, by $10^{-45}$ seconds after the big bang, some serious problems occur. For such non-uniformity to have already existed at $10^{-45}$ seconds after the big bang, matter must have existed in a "peculiar state of extraordinary but not quite perfect order."[2] The placement of molecules in a normal gas, for example, would be far too disordered. For the model to work, the particles in the universe at $10^{-45}$ seconds would have to have been far more perfectly aligned than could be accounted for by chance. The improbable peculiarity of this initial state of order is known as the *smoothness problem*.

A second problem is the puzzle of the *missing magnetic monopoles*. A magnetic monopole is a hypothetical particle believed to possess only one magnetic pole. An ordinary bar magnet, for example, possesses two magnetic poles, a north and a south. A deeper analysis of a bar magnet reveals that its magnetic properties are produced by electric currents circulating at the atomic level. Because a circle or loop of current inevitably produces a pair of opposite magnetic poles—one side of the loop north, and the other, south—all bar magnets are known as *dipoles*, meaning simply that they will always possess a north and a south pole.

Nonetheless, for years physicists wondered if magnetic monopoles or magnetic entities with only a north or only a south pole might exist. In 1931 the British theoretical physicist Paul Dirac even found a niche for them in the mathematics describing some atomic processes. Dirac went on to show that if the magnetic monopole did exist, its magnetic charge would exist only as a multiple of a fixed basic quantity. Unfortunately, exhaustive searches of all manner of rocks, including moon rocks, failed to turn up even one, solitary magnetic charge or monopole.

However, when physicists started proposing various theories to account for the big bang, the mathematics they used to arrive at their models once again suggested the possible existence of magnetic monopoles. Indeed, according to the most credible big-bang models, the universe should be swarming with magnetic monopoles. Further calculations showed that such monopoles would be massive, a million billion times the mass of a proton, or about as heavy as an amoeba. They would also possess a complex internal structure consisting of layers of force much like the layers of an onion. Additional calculations revealed that, given what we know about the magnetic field of the galaxy, monopoles would be outnumbered by atoms in our galaxy by a factor of $10^{20}$, but even this meant that every year about two hundred monopoles would be striking every square kilometer of the Earth's surface. The only problem is that in spite of exhaustive searches no credible evidence has ever been given of their existence.

A third problem concerns the long-standing puzzle of whether the universe is open or closed. Will the universe expand forever, in spite of the fact that its own gravitational self-attraction is constantly fighting to halt its growth? Or is the gravitational self-attraction of the universe strong enough to ultimately halt the expansion and to cause the universe to collapse once again upon itself? The answer to this question involves the relationship between two parameters of the universe known as its *mass density* (also called energy density) and its *critical density*. If the mass density of the universe is equal to its critical density, then the universe is "flat," and its gravitational self-attraction is insufficient to cause it to collapse upon itself (although the expansion rate approaches zero as time increases). In a flat universe the ratio of the mass density to critical density will thus equal 1. If the ratio is equal to 1, it will remain equal to 1 forever. However, it can be calculated that if the ratio was even slightly different from 1 just a few instants after the big bang, the deviation would have grown rapidly with time. For example, if it was greater than 1 it would mean that the universe is closed; if it was equal to or less than 1 it would mean that the universe is open. Given the apparent necessity of this fine tuning, it is surprising that the ratio can today be measured as between 0.1 and 10, so we still don't know if the universe is open, closed, or flat. In order for this value to be within this range today, one second after the big bang the ratio would have had to equal 1 within one part in $10^{15}$. This is such an extraordinarily small number that it suggests that something was wrong with the standard big-bang model. This puzzle, known as the *flatness problem,* was first pointed out in 1979 by Robert H. Dicke and James E. Peebles of Princeton University.

Recently, a thirty-two-year-old MIT particle physicist named Alan Guth has proposed a way to solve some of those problems. Guth's training was as a particle physicist, but in 1979, after hearing Steven Weinberg, University of Texas physicist and author of *The First Three Minutes,* give a talk about the early universe, Guth became intrigued by cosmology. At length, he arrived at a possible solution to the three problems inherent in the big-bang theory. For times later than $10^{-30}$ seconds after the big bang, Guth's picture is identical with the standard big-bang scenario. However, his description of the first instants previous to $10^{-30}$ seconds is radically different from all previous theoretical models and involves a process he calls *inflation.* Before more can be said about Guth's notion of inflation, a few words need to be said about grand unified theories.

According to our current understanding of physics, the universe is governed by four fundamental forces: gravity, electromagnetism, the weak nuclear force that is responsible for radioactivity, and the strong nuclear force that is responsible for the binding together of the protons and neutrons inside the nuclei of atoms. On the surface these forces all seem quite different, but in fact they have a number of similarities. For example, in addition to manifesting as disembodied forces, it is now believed that each force can also manifest as a particle, or *quantum.* The quantum of gravity is now known as the *graviton.* The quantum of electromagnetism is the *photon,* which is also the wave particle of light. The quanta of the weak nuclear force or interaction are known simply as the *weak quanta.* And the quanta of the strong nuclear force that hold or "glue" the nuclei of atoms together have thus been dubbed the *gluons.* The existence of such similarities has caused many physicists over the past decade to put forth various grand unified theories attempting to explain how three of the four forces (gravity being the exception) are really different aspects of the same fundamental superforce. According to current thinking, because of the intense temperatures during the first instants of the big bang the three forces were not yet distinguished from one another and were still all part of the same superforce. It was only in the brief instants following the big bang that this primordial symmetry was broken and the three forces became distinguished.

In grand unified theories this transition—a process called *spontaneous symmetry breaking*—is caused by a shadowy cosmic entity known as a *Higgs field.* The Higgs field, named after British physicist Peter Higgs, pervades space like an invisible fluid and is responsible for determining how the various symmetries were broken. Current theories predict that the Higgs field, like the four fundamental forces, can also manifest as a particle known as a *Higgs particle*—predicted to be a relatively massive particle possessing no spin, a property that can be thought of as roughly analogous to the number of times a particle revolves around its own axis.

According to Guth, in the beginning, the universe accidentally ballooned out of a primordial singularity. For a brief instant all forces and all the constituents of matter were as one. Then, as symmetries began to break via the Higgs field, a hot expansion ensued. At this point, at $10^{-34}$ seconds after the big bang, the uniqueness of Guth's point of view comes into play. Guth explains that the Higgs field supercooled and got stuck, much the same way as a supercooled glass of water can suddenly turn to ice. This resulted in a false vacuum, a vacuum with latent energy or hidden energy, called *false* to distinguish it from empty space. According to understandings already formulated by Einstein in the theory of general relativity, such a false vacuum would have a repulsive force, resulting, says Guth, in an instant of inflation during which time the region that was to become our visible universe exploded from an area one billionth the size of a proton to occupy a region about the size of a baseball.

The notion that the Higgs field might delay its transition and get stuck like a supercooled liquid had first been pointed out by Harvard physicist Sidney Coleman in the mid-1970s. However, according to Guth's first notion of an inflationary scenario, many *bubble universes* could form and collide—universes that start out being completely separate from one another, embedded in the primordial nothingness—thus destroying the observed smoothness of the universe. (Physicists Ian Moss and Stephen Hawking, then both at Cambridge, also advanced similar inflationary scenarios.) Since that obviously has not happened, Guth at first had no solution to the problem. In 1982, A. D. Linde, of the Lebedev Physical Institute in Moscow, and Paul Steinhardt and Andreas Albrecht, of the University of Pennsylvania, pointed out that inflation would stop of its own accord if the Higgs field, instead of being stuck, were merely taking its time—in other words, congealing rather than freezing. If this occurred, a small bubble of ordinary vacuum would have formed and continued to inflate without colliding with other bubbles. A moment later, ordinary expansion would have resumed and the Higgs field would have decayed, refilling the bubble with matter and energy. In some variations of the inflationary scenario, many bubbles might have formed in this process, only

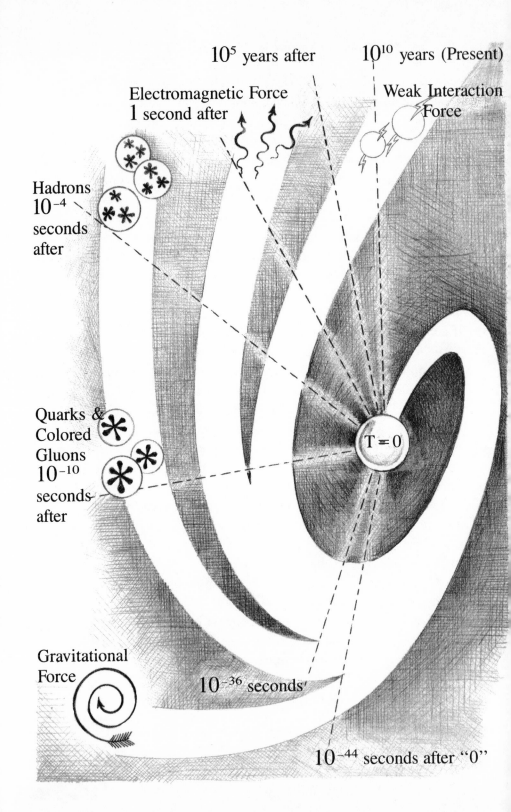

$10^5$ years after

$10^{10}$ years (Present)

Electromagnetic Force
1 second after

Weak Interaction
Force

Hadrons
$10^{-4}$
seconds
after

Quarks &
Colored
Gluons
$10^{-10}$
seconds
after

T = 0

Gravitational
Force

$10^{-36}$ seconds

$10^{-44}$ seconds after "0"

to remain separate island universes forever separated from one another by fortress walls of energy dividing the universe into different domains.

Guth points out that the Higgs field can tie space into a number of other strange and exotic structures that are equally rare. For example, it has the potential to form *strings,* each with the thickness of an elementary particle but millions of light-years long and possessing the mass of several galaxies. (One light-year is 6 trillion miles.) No such strings or domain walls have been found in our visible universe. In fact, if the Earth were to brush up against such a domain wall, it would be instantly destroyed. Such fortress walls of energy might also divide the various possible bubble universes.

Guth believes that in theory it would be possible to perceive a domain wall if one could, say, approach it in a spaceship. "But," he states, "you do have to remember that the distance scales are enormous. In terms of the inflationary universe picture, the distances you would have to go are huge compared to the size of the galaxy. But if you could travel for distances like $10^{35}$ light-years or $10^{50}$ light-years, at those distances you would at least have the possibility of encountering a domain wall. However, if you tried to go through it, your spaceship would just collapse. All of the protons in it would decay."[3]

As to whether such a wall would have dimension or thickness, Guth says, "First of all . . . not all particle theories give rise to domain walls. But some do, and we don't know which ones are

---

Most scientists believe that the universe began with a primordial explosion known as the big bang. According to current understanding, it is believed that at the outset of this explosion, when the starting point of time or T equaled 0, all the fundamental forces had the same strength and all the particles had similar properties. It was only in the infinitesimal fractions of a second after the explosion that this primordial symmetry was broken in a series of steps and the forces and particles divided up into the disparate forms we view them in today.

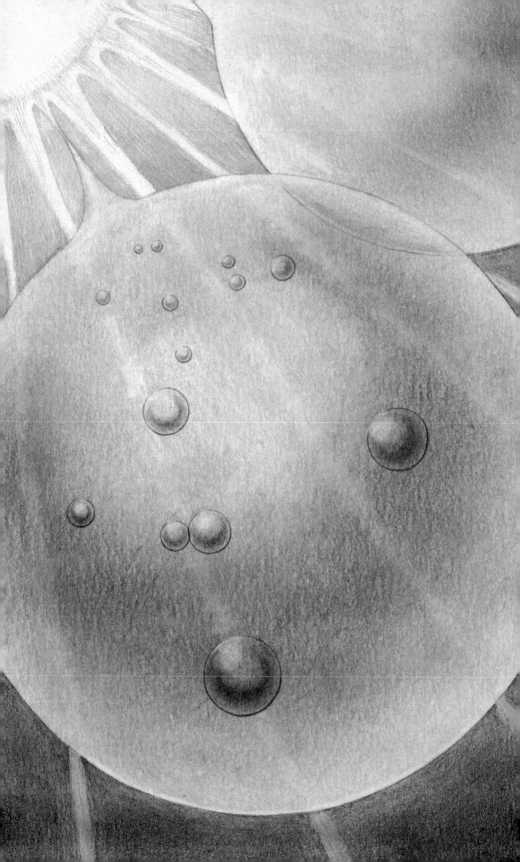

right. So we're only talking about something that's possible. Not something that's really predicted by a well-established theory. But in particle theories that have domain walls, the typical thickness would be ... oh, I think it comes out to about $10^{-28}$ centimeters." They are tremendously thin but, says Guth, "with a tremendously high energy density."[4]

With Guth's inflationary scenario, the horizon problem is avoided. Because the observed universe expanded from such a small initial area, it had plenty of time to homogenize and reach thermal equilibrium. This homogeneous region then inflated to become the observed universe with its uniform microwave radiation background.

The inflationary scenario also explains the mystery of the missing monopoles. As Guth sees it, although they may have been created in great numbers during the big bang, inflation would have diluted them and scattered them throughout the universe so that the likelihood of their presence in any given galaxy would be negligible.

The flatness problem is also resolved in a simple way. Unlike the standard big-bang model, the inflationary model's equations show that the ratio between mass density and critical density are driven rapidly toward 1, no matter what value it had before inflation. Guth thus predicts that the current value of the ratio should actually be 1 and points out that ever more reliable determinations of this value will provide a crucial test for the inflationary model.

As for the smoothness problem, although this issue was actually tackled later, the inflationary scenario has once again come closer to explaining it than any previous theory. In summer 1982, at the Nuffield Workshop on the Very Early Universe held at Cam-

According to the inflationary scenario, our own visible universe may not have been the only universe that formed. In the first burst of expansion following the big bang, other bubble universes might also have formed, like bubbles effervescing in a glass of seltzer.

bridge, a group of leading theorists, including Guth, convened to run a performance test on the inflationary scenario. To do this, they fed their theoretical findings into a computer and then had the computer simulate what a universe that had arisen out of such an inflationary scenario might look like after several billion years. At first the simulation revealed a universe evolving very much as expected. But then, before the simulated universe had reached its current state, its galaxies prematurely collapsed into black holes. Thus, the test was considered a near miss. However, Guth and others were not disturbed, for the inflationary scenario still resulted in a theoretical picture of the early universe that came far closer to reality than any previous models. As theoretical physicist Heinz Pagels of Rockefeller University states, "The particle physics is not right yet." But, Pagels quickly adds, "Inflation will stay. It's the only game in town."[5]

Many physicists agree with Pagels. Says Princeton's Peebles, "The inflationary universe allows the imagination to roam free. Perhaps you start matter roaring around, collapsing and expanding. Somewhere you enter an inflationary phase, and it all happens. From this chaos can pop up this and other universes. It's an enormous breakthrough." He finishes biblically, "Let there be chaos; let there be Guths to straighten it out, to let the crooked places be made straight, and the rough places planed."[6]

With all this talk about planets, particles, and galaxies coming out of the Higgs field and the Higgs field coming out of some sort of primordial unity, one might ask, Where did the primordial unity come from? Certain radical theories suggest that it came out of nothing, a notion based on quantum theory, in which the uncertainty principle predicts that random fluctuations in empty space can instantaneously and without reason create real particles. Thus, the universe and all space and time arose from a small bubble with a nature, says Cambridge physicist Hawking, that is ultimately unknowable. Physicist Paul Davies calls it the interface between the natural and the supernatural.[7]

Physicist Ed Tryon was one of the first to suggest the "something-from-nothing" concept in 1973. As he notes, physical systems are characterized by several types of conserved quantities, such as total energy and mass. If the cosmic total of these quantities was zero, there would be no law to prevent the universe from appearing spontaneously. Since the present energy of the universe may have only been "borrowed" during this period of wild inflation, Guth agrees and says that "the universe may be the ultimate free lunch."[8]

Occasionally when Guth describes his scenario, it becomes apparent that the expansion of the universe occurred at rates faster than the speed of light, suggesting that his theory somehow violates relativity. Guth concedes that he has to go through a short "song and dance" to show why there are really no relativity violations inherent in the scenario. His explanation is based in part on the fact that to a physicist space is not "nothing," but is instead an elastic medium with geometric properties. As Guth says, things traveling within this fabric we call space cannot transcend the speed-of-light barrier. However, general relativity places no limits on how fast the fabric itself can enlarge or stretch.

Guth believes that in spite of these complex notions of false vacuums, dread singularities, spontaneous symmetry breaks, Higgs fields, and domain walls, the universe is still more simple than we had previously thought: "The laws of physics, the fundamental laws that seem to be correct, are remarkably simple in the sense that, given the language of mathematics, you can essentially write the fundamental laws of physics on two pages . . . easily. Our belief is that from the information on those two pages the whole universe emerges with all its complexity, and I think that's amazing."[9]

Guth's views are persuasive but do not yet explain how the universe arrived at its current state. In the next chapter we will examine yet another recently discovered challenge to all theories attempting to describe the processes that brought about the existence of the universe.

# A Hole in the Universe

One problem faced by all theories of the origin of universe is that they must explain how the universe arrived at the state in which we observe it today. In this regard, one puzzle that all such theoretical pictures must tackle is the incredible homogeneity of various aspects of the universe, such as the extremely regular distribution of galaxies throughout the cosmos. The various versions of the inflationary scenario now offered go far toward solving these problems. However, such theories must also be able to explain any rare or unusual features discovered in the large-scale structure of the universe. The more unusual the feature observed, the greater the challenge. Recently, an extraordinary exception to the smoothness of the universe was discovered—a giant tract of emptiness between the galaxies, five times larger than any previously known gap.

The discovery, reported in the September 1981 issue of *Astrophysics Journal,* was made by Robert P. Kirshner of the University of Michigan, Augustus Oemler, Jr., of Yale, Paul L. Schechter of the Center for Astrophysics and Kitt Peak National Observatory, and Stephen A. Schectman of the Mount Wilson and Las Campanas observatories. Kirshner and colleagues in essence took deep-core samples of the night sky. In other words, just as geologists can drill out cylinders of sedimentation from the ocean floor and determine things about the Earth's past by examining the different layers, Kirshner took very precise samplings of light of various small regions of the sky.

To determine which wavelengths of light were reaching the Earth from which regions of the universe, Kirshner and his group relied on a phenomena known as the *red shift*. As is now well known, when the light from a distant object is passed through a spectroscope, the more distant the object, the more the light that comes out of the spectroscope will be shifted toward the red end of the spectrum. By taking very precise samplings of light from the sky and measuring their red shift, Kirshner and his colleagues were able to examine the light as if it were arranged in layers.

In the first round of samplings they took, they found nothing unusual. However, in three samplings from the northern hemisphere, outlining an enormous triangle in the sky, they discovered anomalous gaps in the red-shift distribution. The reason for the gaps was that there were apparently no bright galaxies in the area to confirm the distribution pattern. It was as strange as if geologists, taking deep-core samples from the ocean floor, had suddenly broken through into an immense cavern. Only instead of a cavern, Kirshner and his group had discovered a hole in the universe 500 million light-years beyond the constellation Boötes and 200 million light-years deep.[1]

It is known that there are vast tracts of emptiness dividing the galaxies in the universe. What was unusual about the void discovered by Kirschner was that it was five times larger than any previously known intergalactic wasteland. The discovery sent many theorists scurrying to their blackboards.

Some believe that the hole presents no new problems. Princeton's James Peebles, one of the world's foremost authorities on the large-scale structure of the universe, points out that although galaxies tend to be distributed in space either alone or in small clusters, we know of at least one giant grouping, a community of galaxies known as the Serpens–Virgo supercluster, that is roughly half of the size of the gap found by Kirshner and his colleagues. As Peebles sees it, such lumps and voids are just different aspects of the same problem, a problem involving magnitude. However, Peebles concedes that the Serpens–Virgo supercluster is unique in the observable universe and that it would be extraordinary if holes of such magnitude were found to be common.[2]

Others see the Kirshner void as fuel for new theoretical models. Of these, two have recently received a lot of attention. The first is the so-called *pancakes* (or *blini*) theory of galaxy formation advanced by Ya. B. Zeldovich, J. Einasto, and S. F. Shandarin of the Soviet Union. Expanding upon the laws of hydrodynamics as well as other recent advances in mathematics, Zeldovich and his colleagues propose that the large-scale structure of the universe is really not all that different from physical processes observed on the Earth. Roughly speaking, just as cigarette smoke in a room will level out into sheets, Zeldovich and his colleagues propose that, while matter was still in the gaseous state in the early universe, it also collapsed and accumulated in randomly oriented sheets or *pancakes* with gaps between them. They suggest that the various forces governing the structure of such gigantic pancakes would keep the gaseous matter in them from reexpanding, and eventually gravity would force them to collapse into galaxies. Many theorists have noted that when surveys of galaxies are translated into two-dimensional and even three-dimensional maps, a subtle network of filaments and cell-like walls seems to become visible. Zeldovich and his colleagues point out that their theoretical approach not only explains but demands the existence of such patterns in the large-scale structure of the universe. In other words, just as a large hole may spontaneously form in sheets of cigarette smoke drifting lazily through a room, such a hole might have similarly formed in the early universe.[3]

The second theory also draws on the laws of hydrodynamics and was formulated by Jeremiah P. Ostriker and Lennox L. Cowie of Princeton University. Ostriker and Cowie postulate that small-scale density fluctuations—fluctuations much smaller than those responsible for the formation of galaxies—would have caused massive stars to form early on in the life of the universe. These stars would quickly run through their cycle of evolution and erupt as supernovae, sending shock waves throughout the surrounding gas and piling up matter in so many shells. Within each shell, galaxies would form, more explosions would ensue, and the process would mount, ending with a universe very much like that of Zeldovich, composed of galaxies arrayed in immense flattened superclusters, the remains of the masive shells, surrounding empty holes. Ostriker has pointed out that, in fact, computer simulations of their model have predicted holes of the same magnitude as the great void discovered by Kirshner and his colleagues.[4]

Both models have been criticized. Zeldovich's model requires that certain precise and arbitrary radiation fluctuations had to have occurred in the early universe, the existence of which cannot be proven. Both models are also based on only a small proportion of the total amount of matter in the universe. As we will see in the next section, another problem facing such theories is that most of the matter in the cosmos is "dark," or invisible, and cannot be as readily detected as glowing clusters such as Serpens–Virgo. Because no one is certain what form this dark matter takes, the possibility remains open that the hole in space is really filled with this dark matter and is not a void at all.

# Ninety-seven Percent of the Universe Is Missing

In the night sky can be seen a proliferation of stars and small patches of light that when viewed through a telescope turn out to be galaxies. Astronomers now know that there are literally millions of galaxies out there, and each is composed of billions of stars, as is our own Milky Way. The only problem is that when astronomers add up the mass of all the visible matter in the universe, it accounts for only a small portion of the gravitational field that is apparently stretching and pulling at the fabric of the cosmos. It seems that perhaps as much as 97 percent of the matter in the universe is invisible to us. As Joseph Silk, professor of astronomy at the University of California at Berkeley, states, "Cosmologists have a dire secret. They have not the slightest clue to the nature of the dominant mass constituent of the Universe."[1] Cosmologists are also interested in figuring out where the missing mass is, not only because it will tell us more about how galaxies formed but also because it will answer the key cosmological questions: Is the universe open, and will it go on expanding forever? Or is it closed, and will it ultimately collapse upon itself?

The first hint of a problem came fifty years ago, when astronomer Fritz Zwicky of the California Institute of Technology noticed that a group of galaxies known as the Coma cluster, located 300 million light-years from the Earth, was behaving strangely. As Zwicky observed, the galaxies were moving about in the cluster much more swiftly than expected. Zwicky added up the total amount of light being emitted by the cluster and determined that there was not enough visible matter to account for the gravitational forces holding them together—but, obviously, the cluster was not flying apart. Where, Zwicky asked, was the missing matter?

More recently, in 1973, Princeton astrophysicists Jeremiah Ostriker and James Peebles uncovered evidence that most galaxies seem to possess an invisible halo of mass. In 1974, along with their colleague Amos Yahil, they published further evidence of the existence of such halos, as did J. Einasto, A. Kaasik, and E. Saar of the Estonian Observatory. It began to look as if it were a natural state of affairs for galaxies to have such invisible halos of mass.

In the 1970s, David Schramm of the University of Chicago discovered evidence of missing mass in our own galactic neighborhood. By adding up the total amount of light being emitted by our galaxy Schramm determined that the mass of the Milky Way is equal to the mass of about 100 billion suns. However, the gravitational effects the Milky Way has upon Andromeda, the neighboring galaxy, suggest that it possesses a mass almost ten times greater than can be accounted for visibly.[2] Similarly, Vera Rubin of the Carnegie Institution in Washington, who has spent most of her thirty-odd-year career studying galactic rotations, has discovered, along with her colleagues, that in galaxy after galaxy the observed rotational speed can be accounted for only by a sizable quantity of invisible mass. She observes, "Astronomers can approach their tasks with some amusement, recognizing that they study only the 5 or 10 percent of the universe which is luminous."[3]

What, then, constitutes the invisible mass? One of the first theories proposed that it was simply a gigantic bookkeeping error and that the mass was simply unaccounted-for debris strewn throughout space. However, most researchers now find this notion implausible. In fact, they point out, if the invisible mass were composed of common forms of matter, such as clouds of hot gas, it would be giving off more X-rays than are currently observed. This has caused some researchers to speculate that the missing mass may not even be matter as we know it.

In 1980, experiments in the Soviet Union resulted in findings that, although controversial, suggested another solution. Since 1931, when Wolfgang Pauli first postulated its existence, physicists have known about a fundamental particle called a *neutrino*. Neutrinos are ghostly particles released in certain nuclear reactions. They have no electric charge and very little propensity to interact with matter. This allows them to pass virtually effortlessly through such solid objects as chairs and planets. Moreover, the universe is swarming with these indifferent little ghosts. Trillions are passing through every human being every second of his or her life.

Current theories of the origin of the universe assert that the big bang resulted in a profusion of neutrinos. According to current models, neutrinos should outnumber both protons and neutrons on the order of a billion to one. If neutrinos possessed mass, they could account for the missing mass of the universe.

The Soviet research group discovered evidence that the neutrino was not massless, as had been thought, but actually possessed a tiny mass. At roughly the same time, a team of researchers led by Fred Reines at the University of California at Irvine came up with evidence that the neutrino underwent a phenomenon quantum physicists know as "oscillation." In other words, it was almost as if one type of neutrino would change into a different type of neutrino as it moved along through space. Since, for mathematical reasons, a particle cannot oscillate unless it possesses some mass, the evidence arrived at by Reines and his colleagues was seen as supportive of the Soviet findings.[4] However, both of these experiments are now considered inconclusive.

By summer 1982, researchers from Caltech, the Technical University of Munich, and the Swiss Institute of Nuclear Research had conducted exhaustive searches for neutrino oscillation, with instruments far more sensitive than those used by the Irvine group, and were unable to find evidence of oscillation. They concluded that the neutrino does not oscillate, as had been thought, but this still did not preclude the possibility that it might possess some small mass.[5]

Even if the neutrino does possess a small amount of mass, critics argue that the notion of it being the basic constituent of the universe still has some problems. Mathematical models of how a neutrino-heavy universe would have evolved show that the added mass of such neutrinos would have provided enough gravity to cause the matter in the early universe to coalesce into superclusters, but would not explain how these superclusters in turn coalesced into galaxies.

Some scientists suggest that an even more exotic particle might supply the missing mass. In a 1982 issue of the *Physical Review Letters,* Heinz Pagels, with Joel Primack of Santa Cruz, suggests that the *gravitino,* the particle now believed to be one form in which the gravitational force manifests in the universe, might account for the missing mass. As they point out, like neutrinos, current models of the origin of the universe also propose that large quantities of gravitinos would have coalesced out of the primordial ocean of the big bang. But again the gravitino thesis also has a problem. It is now known that on the large scale, galaxies weave together with one another to form a loose filamentary structure. Although mathematically a neutrino model of the universe can account for the existence of such a filamentary structure, a gravitino model of the universe cannot.[6]

Recently, another candidate for the missing mass has come into the spotlight. In late 1984, Donald W. McCarthy and Frank J. Low of the University of Arizona and Ronald G. Probst of the National Optical Astronomy Observatories announced the discovery of a *brown dwarf,* one of a class of stellar objects intermediate between stars and planets. The object, known as van Biesbroeck 8, has several times the mass of Jupiter and possesses roughly the same composition as a star. However, because it is too small to sustain the fusion reactions necessary to have turned it into a star proper, it glows at a comparatively cool 1,400° Kelvin and is one of the faintest stars known. Astronomers speculate that if many such brown dwarfs exist, they may account for the invisible missing mass. However, final vindication of this theory may be contingent on the development of still more sensitive telescopes.[7]

What is the missing mass composed of? The range of answers to that question only serves to underline our current ignorance. Some have proposed that perhaps the universe is strewn with black holes the size of beachballs and therein rests the missing mass. Others have suggested that one or more of the unending avalanche of particles being proposed today, with such exotic names as the *photino* and the *axion*—might serve as an appropriate deus ex machina. Whatever the case, everyone is in agreement that the answer itself will do two things: First, it will strengthen the strange marriage currently forming between astronomy and particle physics; and secondly, it will answer the question of whether the universe is open and will expand forever, or whether it is closed and will ultimately collapse upon itself in cosmic gravitational annihilation.

It has long been foreseen that gravitation might ultimately cause the universe to collapse upon itself. To determine whether the gravitational pull of the entire universe is powerful enough to halt its expansion, it is necessary to determine the density of matter in the universe. One way of doing this is to calculate how such objects as our own Milky Way should be moving if they are subject only to the smooth flow of the universal expansion and the gravitational tug of the visible matter around them—and then try to measure how they are actually moving. It has recently been argued that the Milky Way seems to be "falling" toward the Serpens–Virgo supercluster mentioned in the preceding section at a rate estimated to be anywhere from 250 to 500 kilometers a second. Fortunately, we are still so far away from the Serpens–Virgo supercluster that it will be many eons before the Milky Way collides with it. Calculations also show that we are falling toward the Serpens–Virgo supercluster much more rapidly than the gravitational pull of the visible matter in the supercluster can account for, once again supporting the belief that galaxies contain halos of invisible mass. Thus, after calculating in the mass of this apparently invisible matter, a much more accurate figure for the matter density of the area can be arrived at. According to several theorists using this method, there is still not enough to halt the expansion. In other words, according to this interpretation, the universe appears to be open.[8]

Not all theorists agree with the view that the unusually rapid rate at which the Milky Way appears to be falling toward the Serpens–Virgo supercluster is due to invisible matter contained within the supercluster. Alan Sandage of the Hale Observatories believes that the apparent falling of the Milky Way is due instead to perturbations on a very large cosmic scale. However, according to Sandage, the universe should still be viewed as open and, indeed, much older than it has previously been considered.[9]

One other argument in favor of an open universe has recently been called into question. The amount of deuterium (an isotopic, or heavy, form of hydrogen, with an extra neutron in its nucleus) in the universe as compared to the amount of hydrogen can only be explained by a certain range of big-bang models—ones that also predict that the universe must be open. The problem is that the matter density predicted by such models is far too low to account for such phenomena as the apparent falling of the Milky Way toward the Serpens–Virgo supercluster.

One of the more curious aspects of the closed-universe model has to do with something physicists call conservation laws. One example is the law of conservation of mass and energy. It is a precisely verified fact that the sum total of mass and energy in a closed system will always remain the same. Some of the energy may be converted into one form or another. For example, chemical energy may be converted to heat energy. Some energy may even be converted into matter and matter into energy. But the sum total of

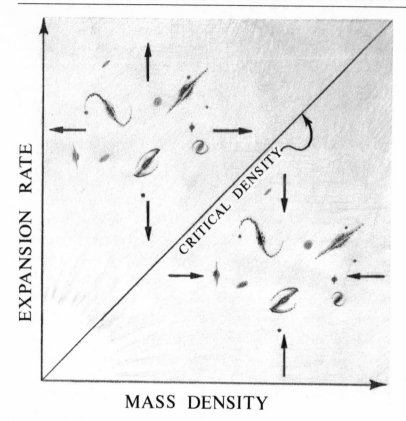

EXPANSION RATE

MASS DENSITY

The critical density is the density of matter in the universe sufficient to produce enough gravitational attraction to hold the universe together. If the amount of mass per volume in our universe equals or exceeds the critical mass, gravity will eventually pull all matter together. If if does not, things will fly apart forever.

all mass and energy in a closed system is an inviolable constant and does not change. This is a fundamental law of physics and is known as the first law of thermodynamics.

Intriguingly, some researchers believe that in the closed-universe model, although the law of conservation of mass and energy holds for all closed systems that we can observe locally, the total mass and energy of the entire universe may not be conserved. Consider a photon emitted from a star. During the emission the energy carried by the photon is exactly balanced by a very tiny decrease in the mass of the star. As the universe expands, the wavelength of the photon increases proportionately, causing the energy of the photon to diminish. However, it can be calculated that if the universe is contracting and the wavelength of the photon is concomitantly contracted, eventually the wavelength of the photon will become shorter than it was at the time of emission. Because of this, some researchers believe that the photon will have gained energy without any compensatory loss of mass or energy in some other region of the universe[10]—a violation of the law of conservation of matter and energy.

Nonetheless, many theorists are in favor of the closed-universe model because they feel that there is something more philosophically appealing about a universe that expands and contracts in great cosmic cycles, rather than a universe that appeared abruptly in a unique event and will go on expanding forever. Others believe that the universe has bounced back and forth in a number of such cosmic cycles, but that it still had a beginning. In an article in the January 1982 issue of *Scientific American,* Duane A. Dicus, John R. Letaw, Doris C. Teplitz, and Vigdor L. Teplitz assert that the energy gained by photons during such periodic cosmic contradictions of the universe might actually be conserved in the next cycle. They state: "If our universe is cyclic, the next cycle should expand for about twice as long as the expansion phase of the current cycle. For earlier cycles the expansion factor would be smaller; we calculate that the present universe is at most 100 bounces from the cycle that lasted just long enough to make a single generation of stars." Concerning this bouncing universe, they add, "The major difficulty for the bounce model is to understand how an extraordinarily inhomogeneous and locally anisotropic universe of isolated, co-alescing black holes can be smoothed out; for that matter, there is no understanding of how a bounce can take place."[11]

Where does this leave us? We do not know what the universe is made of. We do not know whether it is infinite or finite. On the frontiers of the universe, the cosmos is transformed from descrip-tion to question. In the words of the poet Wallace Stevens, "Here, now, we forget each other and ourselves. We feel the absurdity of an order, a whole, a knowledge, that which arranged the ren-dezvous, within its vital boundary, in the mind."[12]

# The Case of the Incredible Shrinking Sun

In 1979 Jack Eddy of the High Altitude Observatory in Boulder, Colorado, announced in the *American Astronomical Society Bulletin* that the Sun was shrinking. He asserted that it was shrinking at such a rate that in 100,000 years it would disappear completely. Eddy, working with mathematician Aram Boornazian, based his findings on a study of measurements of the Sun's diameter that had been made at the Royal Greenwich Observatory between 1836 and 1953. Together they found evidence of a decline in solar angular diameter of approximately .1 percent of the Sun's total diameter per century.[1]

Changes of even a fraction of 1 percent in the size of the Sun can have a pronounced effect on the Earth's climate. There is a great deal of evidence—astrophysical and geological—that the Earth and the Sun have existed in essentially the same relationship to each other for at least 3 billion years.

Some scientists disagreed with Eddy. The calculations from Greenwich that he used had been made by different observers at different times, employing techniques that depended, to some extent, on the expertise of the observers. For example, one technique was the actual measurement of the solar disk by using a micrometer attached to the eyepiece of a telescope. Another was the timing of the passage of the Sun across a fixed meridian wire to calculate its size (taking into account the known rotation of the Earth). Both techniques proved to have been subject to consistent errors, and it was immediately determined that this accounted for at least part of Eddy's findings.

It was also pointed out that changes in the size of the Sun would produce detectable changes in the *solar constant,* the amount of energy it puts out, but no such changes had been observed in measurements since 1850. In a 1980 issue of *Science,* Irwin Shapiro of MIT published an analysis of measurements of the time it took Mercury to pass across the sun's disk—an occurrence that takes place only about thirteen times every century—and concluded that the Sun had maintained a constant size since at least the end of the seventeenth century.[2]

By fall 1980, the issue appeared to be put to rest. But that December, both the leading weekly journals, *Science* and *Nature,* carried articles about work stimulated by the assertions of Eddy and Boornazian. The one published in *Nature* by John Parkinson, Leslie Morrison, and Richard Stephenson again disputed Eddy's claim. However, the article published in *Science* by David Dunham, Alan Fiala, David Herald, Paul Muller, and Sabatino Sofia was more controversial. As their data base, Dunham's group studied measurements made in 1976 and 1979, and they concluded that there had been no change in solar radius between those years. However, they reported that between 1715 and the 1970s, the Sun had shrunk by .34 seconds of arc with a possible range of error of plus or minus .02. Dunham and his colleagues asserted that the Sun was shrinking not at a rate of .1 percent per century, as Eddy and Boornazian had suggested, but at one-tenth that rate, or .01 percent per century, a figure that could still have implications for the Earth's climate for the next hundred years.[3]

Were the findings of Dunham and his colleagues correct? And if so, why did they differ so greatly from Eddy's, and what could explain Parkinson's failure to turn up similar figures? The answer to these questions appeared in late 1981 in a paper by one of Eddy's colleagues, Ronald Gilliland, also of the High Altitude Observatory. Gilliland pointed out that, although Parkinson's group had not uncovered any changes in the solar diameter over long periods of time, their research had uncovered a suggestion of cyclic variations covering a period of about eighty years. This was significant, for Gilliland was aware that eleven-year cycles of sunspot activity also aligned themselves in longer cycles. Eddy's critical interest in the old records of the Royal Greenwich Observatory had been inspired by his curiosity over the relationship between changing levels of solar activity and sunspot cycles.

This furthered Gilliland's interest. Eddy's analysis had indicated a possible correlation between sunspot activity and climate. In particular, Eddy had discovered that the coldest decades in recent history, such as the Little Ice Age of the second half of the seventeenth century, seemed to coincide with intervals when the Sun was remarkably free from sunspots.

Gilliland set out to do a thorough analysis of no less than five sets of data, including the old records from the Royal Greenwich Observatory—correcting, of course, for the errors of certain observers—two sets of Mercury transit observations, solar eclipse data, and measurements of the Sun's diameter made at the United States Naval Observatory in Washington, DC. Gilliland concluded that there had indeed been a decline in solar diameter of about .1 seconds of arc per century since the 1700s. Furthermore, he discovered that the decline followed a repeating rhythm of seventy-six years. This corresponded exactly with the larger cycles of sunspot activity, which also followed a seventy-six-year cycle. Gilliland found a smaller but clearly present fluctuation in solar size that corresponded with the eleven-year sunspot cycles. With caution, Gilliland stated, "Given the many problems with the data sets, one is not inexorably led to the conclusion that a negative secular solar radius trend has existed since A.D. 1700, but the preponderance of current evidence indicates that such is likely to be the case."[4]

With rhythmic variations of eleven years and seventy-six years thus clearly identified, Gilliland concluded that the current shrinking of the sun was simply a phase of an even larger cyclic trend.

This idea also meshed with the substantial astrophysical and geological evidence of the long-term stability of the relationship between the Sun and the Earth. Gilliland posed a further question: What effects might such changes in the diameter of the Sun have on the Earth's climate? To find the answer, Gilliland first had to sort out all the other large-scale factors governing our climate.

In recent years, a geat deal of climatologists' work has been directed toward temperature changes on the Earth. It is generally agreed that during the past century there have been two major factors affecting large-scale trends in temperature. The first is the *greenhouse effect,* the warming effect of increasing levels of infrared radiation accumulating near the surface of the Earth, due to a buildup of carbon dioxide in our atmosphere caused by our increasing use of fossil fuels. The second is the *volcanic,* or cooling, effect caused by dust spewing out in volcanic eruptions, entering the Earth's stratosphere, and blocking out some of the heat of the Sun. Gilliland discovered that by adding a third factor to the calculations—the varying output of solar heat due to the seventy-six-year cycle of variation in the Sun's size—calculations can be brought to match the real temperature record with even greater accuracy.

Gilliland repeatedly points out that his findings are not conclusive and should be considered merely as food for thought. However, by combining the three external influences—the greenhouse, the volcanic, and the solar effects—he has created a simulation of the weather that not only more closely mirrors records of actual temperatures, which have been well established since 1881, but also provides an explanation for some previously unsolved weather puzzles as well. The actual record of temperatures shows that there has been a slight warming of the world from the late nineteenth century up to the 1940s and a subsequent cooling up to the 1970s. Gilliland's three-factor picture explains the warming trend as a combination of solar and volcanic influences, with a twenty-four-year lag between the maximum of the solar diameter in 1911 and the peak warmth of the 1930s—the dustbowl era in the United States. Gilliland also can provide an explanation for the cooling that occurred between the 1940s and 1970s, a time when the concentration of carbon dioxide in the atmosphere was increasing exponentially and should have been increasing the greenhouse effect. In Gilliland's view, the cooling effect occurred in spite of the growing greenhouse effect because it was counterbalanced by the cyclic ebb in solar output. Hence, as he states, "Low temperatures of the past two decades result primarily from a minimum of the solar seventy-six-year cycle."

According to standard calculations of the greenhouse effect, it is predicted that over the next thirty years temperatures on the Earth will rise, on average, a full degree Celsius as ever-increasing quantities of fossil fuel continue to be burned. If Gilliland's conclusions about solar variation are correct, as the Sun reaches the end of its downswing toward the end of this decade, its effects will begin to reverse, instead of counterbalancing the greenhouse effect as it has for the past thirty years, it will start to enhance it. For the next several decades we will see a much more rapid and pronounced warming of the globe than was hitherto thought likely. According to Gilliland's picture, during the 1990s, agricultural conditions will return to a state of fecundity not seen since the unusually beneficial climate that prevailed during the 1950s. However, as we enter the next century, the warming trend will continue, and the forecast shows the development of temperatures and weather conditions unknown on the Earth for a thousand years or more—a super dustbowl era far worse than the 1930s across the Great Plains of the United States. Gilliland's claims are testable, and various studies have been set up that should deny or confirm his findings by the end of the decade.

Fluctuations in the Sun's size are not the only puzzle recently troubling astronomers. Something strange has also been found at the center of the Milky Way.

# Something Strange at the Center of the Milky Way

The centers of galaxies display an unusual range of activity. Some are shrouded in dust; some are dark but pour out radio waves; some are luminous; and some are violent, spewing forth energy and, blowtorchlike, jets of ionized gas. In the past, considerable research has been devoted to the activity observed in the nuclei of many of our neighboring galaxies.

When powerful radio sources were first reported in the heavens in the early 1960s, they were thought to represent a new kind of star. When they were located optically, it was found that they often originated from very bright, starlike objects. However, further studies showed that they were far more distant than might be expected from their brightness. Indeed, they seemed to be among the most distant objects perceived by astronomers and were on the very edge of the visible universe. Because their precise identity remained a mystery, astronomers were not sure whether they should be classified as stars proper and began to refer to them as *quasistellar radio sources*. Hong-yee Chiu at the Goddard Institute for Space Studies in New York later shortened this cumbersome term to *quasar*.

Quasars also appeared to be comparatively small objects, so astronomers also wondered how they gave off such prodigious amounts of energy. Some argued that perhaps some of the findings were in error, and a debate ensued as to whether quasars really were as far away or as powerful as they seemed. It wasn't until the

1970s that new clues emerged that began to resolve the dilemma.

It now seems relatively certain that quasars are, indeed, at the edge of the universe and far more luminous than previously known stellar objects—some as much as 100 trillion times as luminous as the Sun (or a thousand times as luminous as the entire Milky Way galaxy). Quasars are now believed to be otherwise normal galaxies with some sort of power source embedded in their centers. As for what sort of power source might account for the tremendous amounts of light and energy they give off, there is a growing consensus that it may be a black hole. In other words, quasars may be otherwise normal galaxies with active black holes at their centers, rapidly consuming the galaxy from the inside out and converting much of its mass into radio emissions and light.

The concept of a black hole was first envisioned in 1915, when the German astronomer Karl Schwarzschild, on his deathbed, sketched out a mathematical description of what might happen if the gravitational attraction of a mass was so powerful that the mass kept shrinking until it actually collapsed beyond the very fabric of space itself. The description was considered an academic exercise until, decades later, Princeton physicist John Wheeler coined the term "black hole," and the concept took hold. Astronomers are still not certain whether black holes exist, but there is a growing consensus that the universe is probably full of them.

Black holes are now thought to be gravitationally collapsed stars so dense that a spoonful of material from them would weigh more than a billion tons. Originally it was believed that nothing, not even light, could escape from them. For this reason, astronomers first posited that black holes would be completely invisible. However, it was quickly realized that there still might be ways of detecting them. For example, theorists pointed out, if a black hole was close enough to another interstellar object, it might be detected because of the perturbations it caused in the other object's orbit. After astronomers became convinced that black holes existed, the search was on; and in 1973, three separate research groups reported an apparently invisible object gobbling up clouds of hot gas from a star in the constellation Cygnus, the Swan. The object, called Cygnus X-1, is now believed to be the first discovered black hole.

It is now known that, far from being cosmic prisons from which nothing can escape, under certain circumstances black holes can actually function as prodigious generators of energy. Given a sufficiently large hole—perhaps a hole a billion times as massive as the sun—the possible energy that could be produced from such a hole could indeed approach quasar levels.

Such a model could also explain the long torches of matter that shoot out of some quasars. As gas and dust spiral into the hole, the particles tend to be swept into a disklike formation. As the pressure mounts, it can be calculated that some of the material will spew out the axis of the disk in huge jets. This might explain why some powerful radio emissions given off by distant galaxies seem to originate outside the galaxies proper and come from the axis of their galactic disks. If, in addition, the black hole was spinning, it would cause the disk to wobble and to produce spiral jets much like jets of water produced by a spinning lawn sprinkler. Again, such spirals have also been observed.

Some cosmologists think that perhaps all galaxies contain central black holes. Such holes may have formed very soon after the big bang. Hence, quasars—since they lie at distances of 10 to 15 billion light-years away and are thus windows upon the universe as it existed 10 to 15 billion years in the past—are really protogalaxies, showing how all galaxies looked in their infancy. Another school of thought holds that galaxies form first and then the densely packed stars at their centers coalesce and collapse to form black holes. Whatever the process, something strange is happening at the center of many galaxies.

Not surprisingly, interest has focused on the nucleus of our own galaxy. It had been known for a number of years that the core of the Milky Way is a radio source. In fact, it was the first extraterrestrial radio source ever detected, in 1932. In 1977 Kenneth I. Kellerman and his colleagues at the National Radio Astronomy Observatory set about measuring the size of the radio source. From the emissions recorded in these experiments, it was calculated that the radio source existed in Sagittarius A West, presumably at the galaxy's core, and was no more than two hundred astronomical units wide (one astronomical unit is the distance from the Earth to the Sun) or roughly 18 billion miles. Since earlier observations at larger wavelengths had indicated larger widths, it was theorized that scattering of the waves en route had made the source look larger than it actually was. It was further suggested that if the source was scanned at even shorter wavelengths, it would prove to be even smaller.

The source is obscured from us optically by interstellar gas and dust. Infrared radiation does penetrate such dust, but it is absorbed by water vapor in the Earth's atmosphere. It was only recently that a series of large infrared telescopes began operation at high, dry mountain sites such as Mauna Kea in Hawaii, and these provided the first real glimpse of the Milky Way's core. Using the infrared telescope at Mauna Kea, Ian Gatley of the United Kingdom has reported a thin haze of silicate dust around the center of the galaxy. But he found that the dust, instead of completely covering the region, seemed to be distributed in a ring. This indicated that the dust had some processes going on within it that gave it its ringlike shape. As he stated at a 1982 symposium held at the American Physical Society in Washington, DC., "It is not overstating the case to say that the galactic center itself is almost devoid of dust."[1]

An even more intriguing discovery is that the temperature of the dust is a few hundred degrees Kelvin. Although this temperature is low in cosmic terms, it causes the dust to have a total luminosity several hundred million times the luminosity of the sun. Gatley feels that such a phenomenon may be explained by a compact cluster of hot young stars, but he notes that one would need about a thousand young suns jammed into a volume about one light-year across to support the observed data. He concludes, "It is very hard to explain the origin of such a cluster."[2]

In 1979 Robert L. Brown, of the National Radio Astronomy Observatory, obtained a clearer radio picture of the object at our galaxy's core by using the newly completed Very Large Array of radio telescopes in New Mexico. The Y-shaped array, with twenty-seven movable antennas, provided a much clearer picture of radio objects than was previously possible. It showed a spirallike cloud of gas three light-years across at the nucleus of the galaxy, with a very small and exceptionally luminous point in the very center. The object was exactly in the middle of the ring discovered by Gatley.

According to Brown, the gas in the spiral pattern seems to be streaming outward from some central source at a speed of about 260,000 miles per hour or about 350 kilometers per second. One of the arms of the spiral jets seems to be approaching the Earth, and the other receding. This caused Brown to conclude that the source emitting the pair of opposing jets was wobbling back and forth in cycles of about twenty-three hundred years. The source is also observed to vary in intensity from day to day, and since no known physical process can move faster than the speed of light, this ability to vary daily indicates that the source cannot be more than a light-day across, or not much bigger than the solar system. Since only a powerful gravitational force could account for the existence of the spiral jets and the source of the gravitational force is relatively small, Brown concludes that the central object must be gravitationally collapsed—in other words, a black hole.

Further research has indicated that the object at the core is the brightest gamma-ray source in the entire galaxy. Richard Lingenfelter of the University of California at San Diego and Reuven Ramaty of NASA's Goddard Space Flight Center believe that such emissions also indicate the presence of a black hole, for they calculate that if some other phenomenon was causing the radiation, it would produce other kinds of emissions as well.[3] Similarly, using rocket observations of the core region, a Navy group has found

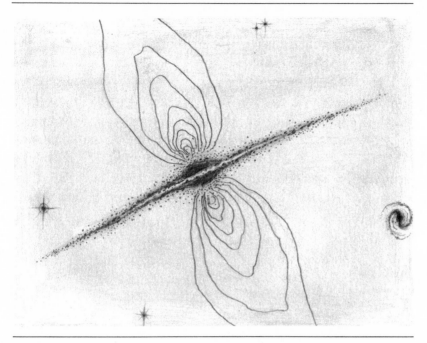

A galaxy like ours seen from the side. Theorists predict that if there is a black hole at its center, a side view should reveal massive plumes of energy spewing forth in opposite directions out into space, as is true of other observed galaxies containing suspected central black holes.

that X-ray emissions are mysteriously lacking. This finding corresponds to a proposal made by Lynden-Bell, that the accretion caused by a massive black hole would, in fact, produce a temperature too low to emit X-rays.[4]

Many researchers now think the object is a black hole, but a few still have their doubts. In an article published in the February 1983 issue of *Nature,* C. H. Townes of the University of California at Berkeley and colleagues argue that for a single source to electrically charge the atoms of both the nearest and the most distant clouds to the observed degree, the luminosity of the object would be at least an order of magnitude brighter than is now observed. They conclude that some observations are suggestive of the presence of a black hole, but others are inconsistent with standard theories; hence, the question of whether or not the source is a black hole must remain open. They concede, however, that "the activity associated with black holes clearly can vary with time; it may have been dominant in this region in the past and is now quiescent. Also, the behavior of a black hole may be much more complex than some of the standard theories allow, and in the face of these many complexities we have no real experience to help understand just what to expect."[5]

# Mining Energy
# from a Black Hole

The first proposal for using black holes as energy sources seems to have been made in the early 1970s by John Wheeler, who had named them, along with Charles Misner and Kip Thorne. In *Gravitation,* they envision an advanced civilization that has enclosed a black hole in a gigantic sphere, with a huge city held firmly to the top of the sphere by the gravitational field of the black hole. Each day millions of tons of garbage from the city could be loaded into shuttle vehicles and dropped toward the hole. As the vehicle spiraled toward the hole, it could eject its garbage, causing the vehicle to gain energy and be sent spiraling back out as the garbage vanished into the hole. The shuttle could theoretically be captured again by the city with the aid of flywheels, transferring its huge kinetic energy to generators that would convert it into electricity. Since the black hole would forfeit some of its mass when it transferred energy to the vehicle, the authors observe, "Not only can the inhabitants of the city use the black hole to convert the entire rest mass of their garbage into kinetic energy of the vehicle, and hence into electric power, but they can also convert some of the mass of the black hole into electric power!" [1]

In the early 1970s another method was suggested by Jacob Bekenstein, then a graduate student at Princeton. While working on his doctoral thesis, Bekenstein noticed that the law specifying the inexorable way a black hole increases its area was strikingly similar to the rules governing entropy. Entropy is, roughly speak-

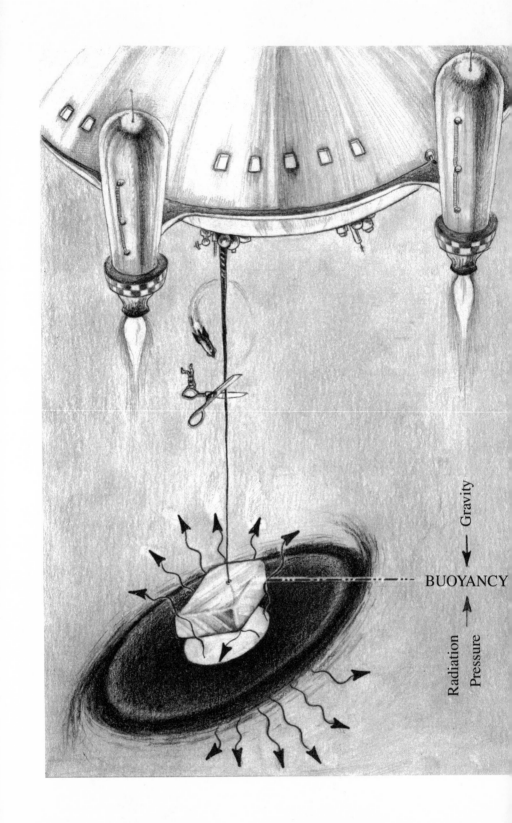

Gravity

BUOYANCY

Radiation
Pressure

ing, the degree of disorder in a physical system. In studying the thermodynamic properties of closed systems, such as the air inside a balloon, nineteenth-century physicists had discovered that such systems tend toward greater states of disorder. For example, if a balloon is filled first with oxygen and then with hydrogen, the law of entropy predicts that, as time goes by, the two gases will get more and more intermixed, or disordered. Physicists call this tendency toward greater states of messiness the second law of thermodynamics.

As it applies to a machine or an engine, entropy is related to the amount of useful energy available. For example, when an engine is functioning, although the aforementioned first law of thermodynamics dictates that the total amount of energy remains the same, the second law of thermodynamics dictates that some of the energy used by the engine will always dissipate and be wasted. Thus, according to the second law of thermodynamics, no engine can ever be a perpetual-motion machine. Put another way, the entropy will always increase; although the amount of energy an engine may produce remains the same, some of the energy will always become more disordered and useless.

In thinking about black holes, Bekenstein started wondering what would happen if a box full of heat radiation was slowly lowered on a rope toward the surface of the black hole, the frontier through which, theoretically, nothing can escape. He then pondered what would happen if the box was opened, its contents emptied into the black hole, and the box withdrawn once again to a

A reflective box filled with heat radiation being lowered into a black hole. Although scientists have long thought that the gravitational pull of a black hole would be too great to allow such a box ever to be retrieved, recent calculations suggest that under certain circumstances the cable supporting such a box could be severed and the box might actually float in the sea of radiation surrounding the black hole in much the same way that a ship floats in water.

safe distance. Bekenstein knew that when the box's heat radiation was discarded into the black hole, the entropy associated with that heat would be lost irreversibly, because the heat would become trapped in the black hole and would never be able to return to the surrounding universe. But Bekenstein also knew that to save the all-important second law of thermodynamics, this reduction in entropy had to be offset by a compensatory increase in entropy somewhere else. Bekenstein proposed that the black hole itself must therefore represent a source of entropy that had previously been overlooked. Since the addition of energy to the black hole would cause its surface to grow slightly larger, Bekenstein concluded that the surface area of the black hole was itself a measure of entropy.[2] Significantly, Bekenstein's theory provided evidence, once again, of the remarkable regularity with which the various laws of physics dovetail. It also suggested another avenue of approach by which the mysteries of black holes might be further unraveled.

Bekenstein's idea was substantiated in 1974, when Stephen Hawking applied quantum theory to black holes and obtained similar insights. One was that the laws specifying the way a black hole increased its area with the acquisition of new materials were in fact identical to the rules governing entropy. Hawking was also the first to demonstrate that black holes are not "black" at all but clothed in a glow of heat radiation now known as "Hawking radiation." Thus, it seemed apparent that the increase in the black hole's entropy accounted for the deficit that would otherwise be caused by the irretrievable loss of ordinary entropy down the hole.

Bekenstein's box experiment turned up another problem. According to our current understanding of physics, the gravitational field of the black hole is so intense that, as the theoretical box is lowered, the total energy content of the box—the heat radiation it contains, as well as the contribution of its rest mass computed from Einstein's famous formula for the conversion of mass into energy, or $E = mc^2$—dwindles to zero. In other words, when the box is opened and the heat it contains is emptied into the black hole, the amount of energy close to the black hole's surface will be substantially less than that originally placed within the box. The problem is that the reduction in the amount of energy released as the box gets nearer the black hole implies less of a boost in entropy for the hole. However, according to the laws of thermodynamics, nature always keeps her entropy books in perfect order. If the boost of entropy received by the black hole is less than the amount of entropy lost to the universe, where did the missing entropy go? It had to be accounted for somewhere, for if it could not be accounted for, the second law of thermodynamics would be violated. If this was possible, perpetual-motion machines might also be possible.

To solve this dilemma, Bekenstein proposed that to balance the entropy books, nature must somehow contrive to prevent any box from getting too close to the surface of a black hole. His solution was sharply criticized. Since the distance allowable would be contingent on the amount of heat radiation in the box, which is in turn contingent on the volume of the box, no one could imagine how or why nature might limit the sizes of boxes plummeting toward the black hole. Recently, however, two other investigators have offered a possible solution. William Unruh of the University of British Columbia and Robert Wald of the University of Chicago point out that for such a theoretical box to be able to contain its heat radiation, its walls must be highly reflective, which would also keep out the Hawking radiation cloaking the black hole. Thus, as the box is lowered, it would displace the heat radiation around the black hole and result in an upthrust on the box in exactly the same way that the displacement of water keeps a boat afloat. As Paul Davies has pointed out, though he would probably "turn in his grave," it is Archimedes's celebrated principle of buoyancy that would keep the box afloat. In fact, Unruh and Wald have calculated that, as the box is lowered, the buoyancy caused by the radiation barrier would ultimately completely compensate for the box's weight. In theory, then, the rope lowering the box could actually be cut and the box would float on its own in the heat bath surrounding the deadly black hole. Unruh and Wald also point out that the effects apparent in this new understanding are just enough to save the second law of thermodynamics.[3]

In 1976 Paul Davies, along with Stephen Fulling, demonstrated that when a mirror is subjected to an acceleration, it emits radiation. Enigmatically, the energy carried by the radiation can, under certain circumstances, have a negative value. As Davies states, "The concept of negative energy is not new in quantum physics, but it taxes our intuition. Energy has a natural zero-point in gravitational physics, where it acts as a source of gravity—recall the equivalence of mass and energy. Zero energy corresponds to the complete absence of gravity. If, by some contrivance, one can reduce the energy of a gravity-free state, then one has produced negative energy. That is what may be achieved by a moving mirror."[4]

Calling upon Davies's work, Unruh and Wald point out that the walls of Bekenstein's box, if reflective, would serve as mirrors. Therefore, as the base of the box spews energy down into the hole, it will also squirt negative energy upward. Similarly, the top of the box will send negative energy upward, while emitting positive energy downward. Inside the box, the negative energy coming up from the bottom will compete with the positive energy coming down from the top, where both types of energy will be trapped by the reflective walls of the box. However, because the base of the box is nearer the black hole, its effective acceleration, and therefore its energy contribution, will be greater. As the box descends, the energy in its interior will become steadily more and more negative. Conversely, as the box is withdrawn, the roles reverse, and the box will become increasingly filled with positive energy. In essence, it will function much the same as a bucket lowered into a well. It will literally pull up energy from the black hole.

In an article in a January 1982 issue of *New Scientist,* Davies observes that no violation of the second law of thermodynamics will be involved, for as the box pulls out energy it will cause the black hole to shrink slightly. Davies also points out that, theoretically, one could simply throw some more matter back into the black hole to keep it from shrinking—perhaps the garbage in Wheeler, Misner, and Thorne's proposed city. Thus, in theory at least, Bekenstein's box would provide a relatively simple way of converting matter into heat energy.

As Davies concludes, however, no one is suggesting that the discovery of Unruh and Wald might really solve the world's energy problems, or that it even remotely corresponds to reality. For the moment, it has simply provided a thought experiment demonstrating that, even under the most exotic circumstances, the second law of thermodynamics is maintained.[5]

Nonetheless, in his book *The Runaway Universe,* Davies has suggested that mining energy from a black hole may not be only the stuff of imagination. He envisions a possible future in which the universe has come almost entirely under intelligent control. In such a universe he imagines technologies capable of prolonging the lifetimes of black holes and continuing to use them for energy long after the stars have all burned out. Perhaps, suggests Davies, the epoch of star-studded skies would linger only as a dim memory. But instead of resulting in chaos, black holes would provide the means for such a galactic civilization to survive through eternity and avoid the fate predicted by Erasmus Darwin, who wrote:

> Star after star from heaven's high arch shall rush,
> Suns sink on suns, and systems systems crush,
> Headlong extinct, in one dark centre fall,
> And death, and night, and chaos mingle all!

# The .001557806449023-Second Pulsar

The activity going on at the center of the Milky Way is not the only recently discovered anomaly in the heavens. Astronomers have also located another exotic object, one believed to belong to an entirely new class of stellar phenomena.

The path to this discovery began in August 1967, when a Cambridge graduate student named Jocelyn Bell discovered what she described as an anomalous "bit of scruff" in a readout of radio signals coming from the night sky. Bell told her thesis adviser, Antony Hewish, about the finding. At the time, because it fit no known phenomenon, it was assumed to be of local origin and dismissed. Later that year, Bell saw the scruff again and explored the matter further, tracing its place of origin to the constellation Vulpecula, the Little Fox, a dim constellation that straddles the Milky Way just south of Cygnus. Intrigued by the discovery, both she and Hewish found that the radio source was pulsing once every 1.33730113 seconds. Moreover, its pulse was extremely regular, accurate to 1 part in 10 million.

Bell and Hewish went on to discover several other rapidly pulsing radio sources and realized that they were onto something. At first they actually considered that the pulses might be radio signals from alien civilizations and even named them LGM-1 through LGM-4, the letters standing for *little green men*. However, if the signals were coming from planets inhabited by other civilizations, the Cambridge group reasoned that the red shift of the pulses should vary slightly as the orbit of their respective planets periodically took them in directions of movement away from the Earth. When it was discovered that this was not the case, the little green men hypothesis was dismissed. Hewish named the radio sources *pulsars* and set out to discover what sort of natural phenomenon might account for such extremely regular radio emissions.

His search finally led him to resurrect the almost-forgotten concept of *neutron stars*. Neutron stars had first been proposed in the early 1930s by Fritz Zwicky and Walter Baade. In calculating what might happen when a massive star went through its death throes, Zwicky and Baade suggested that, perhaps, as its fuels burned out and it collapsed, a star would reach a state when its matter became so dense that the atoms composing it would also collapse, all the electrical charges of its protons and neutrons would cancel each other out, and it would become little more than a gigantic neutron. As Zwicky and Baade noted, a teaspoon of matter from such a superdense star would weigh many tons. Just before Hewish's search, Alastair G. W. Cameron of NASA's Institute for Space Studies in New York had also resurrected the idea of neutron stars to try to explain certain brilliant X-ray emissions that had been discovered coming from various points of the sky. Cameron suggested that such superdense stars might alternately expand and contract like a beating heart, and it was this feature that drew Hewish to the concept as a likely candidate for the pulsars that he and Bell had discovered.

Shortly thereafter, Thomas Gold of Cornell University refined the idea and proposed that it was not oscillations that were causing the pulsars to pulse. As he pointed out, when figure skaters start spinning with their arms outstretched and then pull their arms in, their spin rate increases. Similarly, Gold noted, as a neutron star contracted, its rate of spin would also increase. Gold calculated that the rate of spin for such a contracting neutron star would be extraordinarily fast. For example, if a star the size of the Sun, which spins at the rate of one rotation per month, collapsed to the assumed ten-kilometer diameter of a neutron star, its rate of spin would increase to an astounding thousand times per second. Gold further noted that such a neutron star's magnetic field, also greatly compressed by the star's collapse, would cause the ionized gas, or plasma, surrounding the star to spin. This would cause the star to emit highly directional beams of radiation along the lines of its magnetic field, in much the same way as a lighthouse emits beams of light. Perhaps it was just such a beacon, said Gold, that was being picked up by Bell and Hewish as the pulsar's periodic flashes of radio waves.

Gold also made several predictions about the behavior of such neutron-stars-turned-pulsars. First, he noted that they would probably be found near the remains of supernovae, massive stars that had exploded. Secondly, he predicted that although their oscillations were very regular, their radio pulses would be found to be decreasing gradually as the spin rate of the star itself inevitably decreased.

To check Gold's predictions, researchers made more precise measurements of the oscillation rate of the various known pulsars and discovered that they were gradually decreasing. In 1968, David H. Staelin and Edward C. Reifenstein III turned the three-hundred-foot dish of the National Radio Astronomy Observatory in Green Bank, Virginia, toward the Crab Nebula—a location where, in 1054, Chinese astronomers had recorded the explosion of a supernova. Staelin and Reifenstein found, as Gold had predicted, that at the center of the expanding gas cloud left by the supernova, there was indeed a pulsar flashing at the rate of thirty times a second. Until recently, this was the fastest known pulsar; of the many dozen now known, most average about one flash per second. Given that the pulsar at the center of the Crab Nebula had appeared only 914 years earlier, this corroborated Gold's theory perfectly. The belief that pulsars are rapidly spinning neutron stars passed from the realm of theory into the realm of fact.

Recently a new type of pulsar has been discovered—one that beeps at the phenomenal rate of 642 radio flashes per second. In other words, a day—the amount of time it takes the new pulsar to complete one orbit—is about .001557806449023 seconds. The new pulsar is called 4C21.53. Like Bell's LGM-1, it also lies in the direction of Vulpecula, approximately fifteen thousand light-years from the Earth. It is a ten-kilometer ball of nuclear matter (matter so dense that free protons and electrons are virtually nonexistent) spinning 642 times a second. Its rotational kinetic energy is comparable to the total energy output of a supernova. Its surface gravity, roughly a trillion times that of the Earth, is just barely strong enough to keep the object from flying apart, and it is spinning about its axis so rapidly that an object at its equator would be moving at one-fifth the speed of light.

It was in 1979 that Donald Backer of the University of California at Berkeley first detected 4C21.53's beam sweeping across the Earth. Backer's instrumentation picked up 4C21.53's beacon only briefly, but it provided him with enough information to perceive its peculiarity immediately. He spent the next five years looking for 4C21.53 again, but it wasn't until November 14, 1982, at the Arecibo radio telescope in Puerto Rico that he verified its existence.[1]

Might such an exotic object have any sort of practical use? Backer has offered the suggestion that 4C21.53, now called the Millisecond Pulsar, might be used as a clock. The Naval Observatory claims that its atomic timepiece is accurate to one part in $10^{14}$. If it remains stable, the Millisecond Pulsar is far more accurate than that. However, some pulsars show tiny random glitches in their frequencies due to shifts in their crusts. Although the Millisecond Pulsar has not yet exhibited such instability, there is always the possibility that it might. But if it doesn't, Backer notes that it could possibly turn out to be the most accurate timepiece in the galaxy.

Other behaviors exhibited by the Millisecond Pulsar are even more intriguing. Because it was beeping so fast, it was at first believed that it must be a very young pulsar, practically newborn. After several weeks, however, Backer and his colleagues ruled out this possibility. The Millisecond Pulsar was not surrounded by a gaseous supernova remnant, which would indicate that it came from a relatively recent supernova explosion. Its magnetic field was also quite weak, unlike a new pulsar's, and its surface temperature was 1.5 million degrees Kelvin, cool compared to what would be expected of a new pulsar. These facts indicated that the Millisecond Pulsar was actually billions of years old.

How then, scientists wondered, had the Millisecond Pulsar acquired its phenomenally rapid spin? Within months after the Millisecond Pulsar's discovery, theorists rose to the challenge and constructed a possible picture of why it rotated so fast. The most persuasive suggested that the pulsar was originally part of a double or binary star system, two ordinary stars in orbit around one another, and at one time had a companion star. This is not unreasonable, for numerous such partnerships are known to exist in the universe. According to Jacob Shaham and colleagues of Columbia University, along with A. Cheng of Rutgers, as the pulsar cooled down, matter from its companion started to pour into it, perhaps because the companion swelled into its red giant phase or perhaps because the binary orbit shrank due to gravitational radiation. Whatever the case, the falling matter streamed onto the pulsar

---

The millisecond pulsar rotates around its axis at the phenomenal rate of 640 times a second. Some scientists believe that it acquired such a remarkable rate of rotation because it was fueled by a stream of gas drawn from an unseen companion. The reason that pulsars are seen to pulsate by Earth astronomers is that their magnetic poles, like the Earth's own magnetic poles, do not appear to be centered on the pulsar's axis of rotation. This would account for the fact that radiation beams coming from the star, like the rapidly turning beam of a lighthouse, are perceived by Earth astronomers to sweep through the heavens 640 times a second.

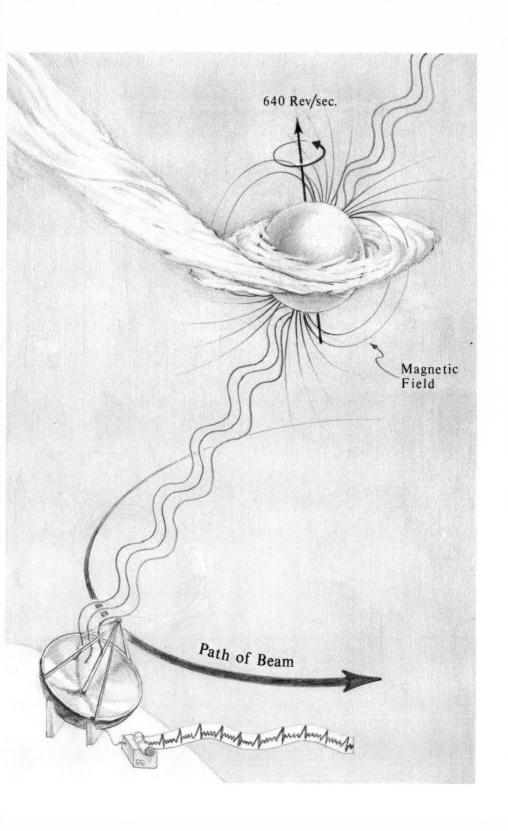

640 Rev/sec.

Magnetic
Field

Path of Beam

surface in rapid spirals, forcing it to spin faster and faster until, in the end, it completely dissipated its companion. It is estimated that at this point the pulsar may have been spinning at a rate of nearly a thousand times a second.[2]

If this is, indeed, the explanation, given that binary systems are common in the galaxy, some astronomers were hopeful that millisecond pulsars would shortly be found to be equally numerous throughout the heavens. Others remained convinced that the Millisecond Pulsar was an isolated phenomenon. The truth, at the moment, is somewhere in between. In 1983 a second millisecond pulsar was reported; but to obfuscate the matter further, although the predicted flood of millisecond pulsars has not manifested, tantalizingly, the second one has been found to be the primary member of a binary-star system.

As for what this means, or why only two millisecond pulsars have so far been found—the opinions on the matter are as numerous as the questions. In the meantime, the only thing that is certain is that our current understanding of pulsars is certainly due for further and rapid change.

# The Age of the Universe Crisis

Scientists currently use several methods in attempts to measure the age of the universe. One is to measure the amounts remaining in the universe of certain radioactive isotopes, believed to have been left over from the big bang. A second method is to calculate the age of the stars in the universe, based on what is now known about stellar evolution. A third and final gauge of the universe's age is to take the rate at which the cosmos is expanding and, from that rate, calculate how much time seems to have elapsed since the big bang. The problem is that each of these methods gives different results, and cosmologists are currently in a quandary as to how to rectify the conflicting figures.

The first method, nuclear chronology, is based on the fact that radioactive isotopes have very specific and readily determinable rates of decay or *half-lives*—the amount of time it takes for 50 percent of a population of identical particles to decay. For example, astronomer and "nucleocosmochronologist" David Schramm points out that an isotope of a rare metallic element known as rhenium is ideal for such studies because its half-life is much greater than even the oldest theorized ages of the universe. The only uncertainty in using isotopes such as radioactive rhenium is that their abundance in the early universe can only be derived from current theories of star formation. Nonetheless, Schramm believes that a reasonably accurate lower bound on the age of the universe can be arrived at from this method and estimates that the minimum age of the universe is 8 billion years. He admits, however, that if supernova explosions in the universe added significantly to the amount of radioactive rhenium extant in the cosmos, the minimum age of the universe might then be pushed to anywhere from 11 billion to 17 billion years.[1]

According to most theoretical models, the first stars in the universe were born fairly soon after the big bang, when the universe still consisted mainly of dense gas. From this it is concluded that the age of the oldest stars should also give us a good indication of the age of the universe. It is currently believed that the most ancient stars occur on the outskirts of galaxies in huge globular clusters of a million or more suns apiece. Such stars, all believed to have been born at roughly the same time, exhibit a range of masses. Because heavier stars are hotter and brighter and burn themselves out more quickly than their smaller and cooler relatives, the age of the stars in such a group can be determined by comparing the number of hot bright stars left in the cluster against the total number of stars remaining. Using this method, astronomers have determined that the age of the oldest stars in the universe is somewhere between 15 and 19 billion years.

By combining both of the above methods, Schramm believes that the age of the universe can be placed more accurately at no less than 13.5 billion and no more than 16 billion years old.[2]

The third method, tracing back the expansion of the original big bang, is also the oldest approach. As long ago as 1917 German astronomer Carl Wirtz called attention to the fact that there was a correlation between the distances of various spiral nebulae and their velocity of recession, but the idea remained tentative until 1927, when Edwin Hubble measured the Sun's velocity of rotation in our own galaxy. In a paper titled "A Relation between Distance and Radial Velocity Among Extra-Galactic Nebulae," he pointed out that the farther away a galaxy lies, the greater its red shift and hence its velocity. With this discovery Hubble was able to calculate the rate at which the universe was expanding and to quantify it numerically in a quantity called the Hubble constant, or $H_0$ for short. Hubble determined that this rate was about 100 miles per second per million light-years. In other words, for every million light-years farther out a galaxy was located, it would recede at an additional hundred-miles-per-second velocity.

Not long after its inception, other astronomers started to gather evidence that called for a revision in the Hubble Constant, and its precise value has been the subject of debate ever since. In the past decade, astronomers have divided into two camps over the matter: one, headed by Hale Observatory astronomers Allan Sandage and Gustav Tamman, assigns a value to $H_0$ equal to 50 kilometers per second per megaparsec (a megaparsec is 3.26 million light-years); the other, promoted by University of Texas astronomer Gerard de Vaucouleurs, advances a value of 100 kilometers per second per megaparsec. Both these estimates are considerably lower than Hubble's originally supposed value. Both sides are in rough agreement on the value for the constant for galaxies out to 13 million light-years (4 megaparsecs), but beyond that the distance scales vary by a factor of two, and so does the derived age of the universe.[3]

In recent years, yet another value for $H_0$ has been suggested. In 1977 Brent Tully and Richard Fisher discovered that a galaxy's brightness is also closely related to its rotation speed, which can be determined quite accurately. Thus, by comparing the brightness predicted by the Fisher–Tully relation with the galaxy's apparent brightness, another estimate of the galaxy's distance can be determined. This method has in turn suggested that perhaps an intermediate value for $H_0$ of 85 kilometers per second per megaparsec is the most accurate.

This new figure suggests that the age of the universe is somewhere in the neighborhood of 12 billion years. Some have suggested that the only way to reconcile an age of 15 billion, as suggested by the other two methods of determining age, and a Hubble constant equal to 85 kilometers per second per megaparsec is to postulate that some sort of repulsive force is accelerating the separation of the galaxies. This brings the matter into a curious full circle, for at one time in his life Einstein had predicted the existence of just such a repulsive force to account for why the combined gravitational force of the entire cosmos had not caused the unverse to collapse upon itself long ago. Einstein called his proposed repulsive force the *cosmological constant* but abandoned the idea when it was discovered that the universe was expanding and that was why it had not collapsed.

Does this mean that Einstein's cosmological constant should be resurrected? Most theorists think not, for calculations show that if such a mysterious repulsive force did exist in the universe, most of the galaxies and quasars visible in the heavens should also have the same degree of red shift. This is not the case.[4]

Hubble's assumption that the universe is expanding at a constant rate also turns out to be incorrect. For example, we now know that the rate at which our own galaxy is moving in the overall expansion of the universe is being affected by the gravitational pull of the Serpens–Virgo supercluster. It is also known that this sort of gravitational clumping is commonplace in the universe. In other words, all the objects in the universe are being so tugged and pulled by all of the other objects in the universe that it is difficult to establish what the overall expansion rate is. In spite of this fact, most theorists still feel confident enough about estimated values of $H_0$ to believe that the resulting calculated 12-billion-year age of the universe is still reasonably accurate.[5]

Thus, the age of the universe crisis continues, and no one knows why the various methods currently employed produce such disparate results. In the final analysis, the age of the universe remains unknown. In the words of Hubble himself, "The explorations of space end on a note of uncertainty. . . . We measure shadows. We search among ghostly errors of measurement."

# Part II

---

# THE QUANTUM UNIVERSE

J ust as science has explored the far reaches of the cosmos to an extent never before imaginable, it has also probed ever deeper in the other direction, into the realm of the quantum. Whereas our role in reinventing the universe may seem less apparent in light of the seemingly reliable and steadfast observations made by astronomers, it becomes far more apparent in exploring the landscape of the atom. As Paul Davies notes, quantum physics "restores mind to a central position in nature. . . . The act of observation in quantum physics is not just an incidental feature, a means of accessing information already existing in the external world; the observer enters the subatomic reality in a fundamental way, and the equations of quantum physics explicitly encode the act of observation in their description." [1]

Just as the answers to certain cosmological questions depend on puzzles involving the atom, certain mysteries in the atom also depend on the answers to questions about the cosmos as a whole. As we will see, continued probing into the quantum realm has further strengthened the marriage between cosmology and particle physics. In this section we will find that just as quantum physics continues to discover new particles and new forces, it also continues to find still further indications that the universe is an invention, that there are levels of reality that cannot be said "objectively" to exist, and "particles" that physicists openly confess are as much theoretically convenient as they are real. We will also find that quantum physics is on the verge of inventing the most remarkable metaphor of all, a theory that explains how all the forces of nature may be united in a single and fundamental superforce.

# Quantum Theory Comes of Age

Quantum theory was born in the first decades of the twentieth century and was largely fathered by two men, the German physicist Werner Heisenberg and the Danish physicist Niels Bohr. According to Bohr and Heisenberg, the subatomic realm was a landscape in which common-sense notions of distance, times, and a strict division between consciousness and reality ceased to exist. Ever since they advanced this notion, physicists have wondered about the correctness of quantum theory. Einstein himself was convinced that the strange and sometimes nonsensical world described by quantum theory indicated that the theory itself was somehow wrong or incomplete. Until his death he held on to the belief that the day would come when a more complete picture of subatomic reality would be formulated, and common-sense notions would once again prevail.

One of the problems long inherent in quantum theory is that the basic constituents of matter do not behave in ways that seem consistent with our practical understanding of the world. As a matter of fact, these basic particles cannot even be said to be "objects" as we usually conceive them. At the beginning of the twentieth century, physicists were confronted with a body of raw data that needed an organizing metaphor. The idea of the electron was proposed by British physicist J. J. Thomson. However, no one has ever seen an electron, and no one ever will. All that is ever seen is a flash on a fluorescent screen. Although it is generally agreed that the ability to predict the electron's activity is proof of its reality, some have argued that an electron exists more as a concept than an entity in the real world. According to this way of thinking, the reason that predictions can be made today is because the electron was constructed to fit earlier experiments. It is interesting to note that entirely different constructs can be invoked, using the same raw experimental data, and can allow scientists to make different but equally valid predictions. For example, in the early days of quantum physics, Heisenberg put forth a "matrix theory" and Erwin Schrödinger a theory of "wave mechanics"; although very different constructs, their theories turned out to be mathematically equivalent. As poet and physicist William Empson has written:

> All physics one tautology;
> If you describe things with the right tensors
> All law becomes the fact that they can be
> described with them;
> This is the Assumption of the description.[1]

Another assertion of quantum theory, and one that troubled Einstein, concerns the properties of certain pairs of particles produced by some atomic processes. For example, in one such process that produces a pair of photons, the wave-particles of light, it is known that the two photons produced will continue to behave as if they were strangely connected to each other, no matter what the distance separating them. For instance, after such twin photons are produced, if one photon is allowed to zoom off toward one side of the galaxy at the speed of light, and the other photon is allowed to do the same in the opposite direction, when received by observers stationed on opposite sides of the galaxy, certain measurements made on the two photons will still be found to be correlated.

Einstein was so skeptical of this assertion that in 1935, along with his colleagues Boris Podolsky and Nathan Rosen, he published a paper titled "Can a Quantum-Mechanical Description of

Physical Reality Be Considered Complete?" In the paper Einstein pointed out that if certain properties of twin particles were always found to be correlated, the finding would imply, among other things, that there existed a signaling process that was instantaneous and thus faster than the speed of light. Since faster-than-light communication was strictly forbidden by special relativity, Einstein concluded that quantum theory must therefore be incorrect or incomplete.

What Einstein failed to recognize was that he had based his reasoning on an assumption that later physicists have been more reluctant to make. He assumed that quantum reality was *objective* in the sense that the term is used in classical physics. In 1964 John Bell, a physicist at CERN, the European Organization for Nuclear Research in Switzerland, took this error into account and formulated an elegant and brilliant mathematical proof known as Bell's inequality theorem. Bell realized that if measurements performed on two such particles were found to have a greater degree of correlation than could be predicted by chance, it didn't necessarily mean that any faster-than-light signaling proces had occurred. Such correlations could also be explained if it were assumed that subatomic reality was *non-local*. No matter how far apart from each other such particles seem to be, at our own level of reality, at the subatomic level they are not separate at all; at that level reality is nonlocal, and all portions of the universe are infinitely interconnected. From this premise, Bell demonstrated that only two options were possible: Quantum theory was incorrect; or, if quantum theory was not in error, either objective reality did not exist at the subatomic level, or all portions of the universe were infinitely interconnected.

Even more important than Bell's lucid assessment of the matter was the fact that he sketched out an actual experiment that would resolve the issue once and for all. For the first time in its sixty-odd-year history, one of the most controversial predictions made by quantum theory could be put to the test.

Among the first researchers to test Bell's formulation were John Clauser and Stuart Freedman of the Lawrence Berkeley Laboratory. In 1972 they devised the following experiment: A photon source was set up to produce the sets of twin photons. After they were emitted, the photons were sent flying off in opposite directions, each toward a polarizing filter, beyond which was a photomultiplier tube set up to register the impact of the photons. The reasoning behind this was that, when the polarizing filters were set at certain angles, the photomultipliers would detect a greater degree of correlation between the polarizations of the two photons than that predicted by chance alone.

After performing their experiment, Clauser and Freedman discovered that the behavior of the particles did, in fact, support the predictions made by quantum theory.[2] This was important, for it strongly suggested that quantum theory was correct; if quantum theory was correct, as Bell had pointed out, either the universe was not objective or subatomic relity was nonlocal. Unfortunately, although Clauser and Freedman laid most of the important groundwork, there were several potential flaws in their experimental setup. Critics argued that the photomultipliers used were not 100 percent efficient, and the polarization filters or analyzers used did not perfectly pass or block the photons traveling through them.

It wasn't until 1982 that Alain Aspect, along with colleagues P. Grangier and G. Roger, devised an experiment that fulfilled the requirements posed by critics. First, the analyzers used were set up thirteen meters apart, so there was no chance that the two photons were interacting with each other through any known causal process. They also employed the newest in high-tech equipment, switching devices so rapid and precise that the devices were able to adjust the angle of the polarizing filters after the photons of light had left their sources but *before* they had had a chance to traverse the full width of the room. Consequently, any signal traveling between the analyzers and containing information about the switching direction would have to travel faster than light to influence any

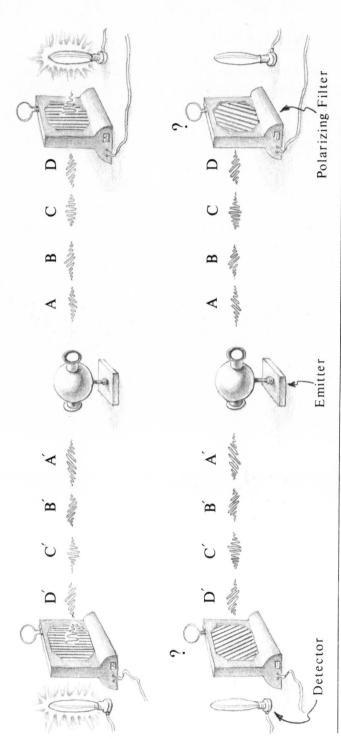

Detector       Emitter       Polarizing Filter

*Above:* The emitter shoots out matched pairs of particles, symbolized by A and A´, etc. Because both members of a pair possess identical polarities, either the detectors behind both polarizing filters will be activated or neither will. *Below:* Each detector is charged so that it measures a different angle of polarization while the matched particles are in flight. When this is done, the correlation between the responses from the two detectors is difficult to explain without assuming instantaneous communication between the pairs of particles.

measurements. The experiment was performed and the predictions of quantum theory were correct.[3]

There is now no longer any doubt. "Local hidden variables theory is dead," announced Syracuse University physicist Fritz Rohrlich in the September 23, 1983, issue of *Science*. Hidden variables theory was the notion that some other phenomenon, some "hidden variable," might explain the apparent nonlocal communication between particles predicted by quantum theory; for decades it had remained a possible deus ex machina until the Aspect experiment knocked it down.[4] Quantum theory has come of age, but this, of course, brings us face-to-face with Bell's original warning. Quantum theory, the belief that reality is local and that all points in space and time are separated, and the assumption that reality is objective cannot all be correct. If it can now be stated with conviction that quantum theory must stand as a correct view of reality, which of the other two cherished ideas must go?

Some, such as physicist David Bohm, feel that our belief that all points in space and time are separate must be amended. He asserts that, to understand the world of the quantum, we must postulate the existence of a higher "multidimensional" ground, in which all points in space and time are infinitely interconnected.[5] Others, such as physicist Heinz Pagels, feel that there is a nonlocal correlation between the two particles, but that no information is conveyed and thus no higher multidimensional ground need be postulated.[6]

Whatever the interpretation, one thing is now certain. In the areas where it is currently applied, quantum theory has been vindicated as a paradigm. This is fortunate, for, building upon the foundation laid by the quantum theorists, physicists have now gone far beyond the understandings of Bohr and Heisenberg. In the next chapter we will find that they have begun to decipher the secrets of the forces responsible for the creation of the quantum world itself and, in doing so, have perhaps uncovered the way that all the laws of nature fit together.

# Broken Symmetries and Grand Unified Fields

Most physicists believe that the myriad of physical phenomena—indeed, all the workings of the universe—are the interactions of four basic forces: gravity, electromagnetism, the strong nuclear force that binds the nuclei of atoms together, and the weak nuclear force that is responsible for radioactivity. It was Einstein's dream that the mathematical formulations describing two of these forces—gravity and electromagnetism—might someday be integrated into a single coherent theory, a *unified field theory*. Einstein did not live to see his hopes realized. Physicists have continued to struggle to arrive at some mathematical understanding that would encompass all four of nature's forces. Today, many scientists hope that all four forces can be unified in one sweeping and mathematically elegant construction that would explain all of the operations of nature.

The quest toward a unified understanding of the forces of nature began in the 1850s, when the physicist James Clerk Maxwell demonstrated that two distinct forces of nature, electricity and magnetism, could be understood as different facets of a single, unified field—the electromagnetic field. From this understanding, Maxwell determined that some of the solutions to the equations responsible for unifying the two forces could also be expressed as sine functions, which meant that the electromagnetic field could be visualized as periodic undulations or waves propagating through space. From his equations Maxwell determined the speed of such waves and found that they exactly equaled the speed of light. The conclusion was unavoidable that light must be considered an electromagnetic wave. Extrapolating from this realization, Maxwell was able to predict the existence of other electromagnetic waves that could logically be assumed to exist at other wavelengths. Heinrich Hertz's subsequent discovery of radio waves confirmed one of Maxwell's predictions, as did the discoveries of X-rays and gamma rays.

The fact that two distinct forces of nature, electricity and magnetism, could be understood as different facets of a more inclusive concept, the electromagnetic field, was part of the reason Einstein sought to incorporate still other forces of nature into even larger conceptual understandings. However, it wasn't until 1958, over a hundred years after Maxwell's tour de force, that Sheldon Glashow, then still a graduate student, saw a way that a theory might be formulated that would unify electromagnetism with the weak nuclear force. This was a startling concept, for on the surface electromagnetism and the weak force appear even more disparate than electricity and magnetism. For example, the effects of electricity and magnetism are quite apparent on the level of everyday life, and electromagnetic waves can exert their influence over vast distances, even across the length of the universe. Conversely, the weak nuclear force can only exert its influence over distances equal to about one-hundredth of the diameter of the nucleus of an atom.

In spite of the dramatic differences between the two forces, Glashow noticed tantalizing similarities between their respective interactions. The electromagnetic interaction between two charged particles could be thought of as basically the exchange of a photon, or quantum of light, between particles (a notion already well accepted in physics). In other words, the photon might be thought of as the messenger particle of the electromagnetic force. Glashow's theory suggested the existence of a similar particle called the *W particle* that would function as a messenger particle for the weak force. According to Glashow's calculations, the W particle, like the photon, would have a spin of one unit. However, unlike the photon, which is massless, the W particle would be relatively massive, somewhere in the neighborhood of eighty times the mass of a proton. Glashow suggested that perhaps the extreme difference between the range and strength of the two forces was due to the difference between the masses of their messenger particles. In other words, the photon is able to operate over long distances because it is massless, but the influence of the weak force is limited to a very small range because of the comparatively large mass of its messenger particle, the W. Although some of Glashow's ideas were not new, he did make one further and radical new assertion. He claimed that his theory would lend itself to a mathematical process known as *renormalization*.[1]

Renormalization is, at first glance, a process Lewis Carroll might have invented. It came about as a result of the *Alice in Wonderland*-ish world physics encountered in the subatomic realm. At one time, the electron was viewed as an object. Just as the Earth exists in three dimensions and is surrounded by a gravitational field, it was believed that the electron was a similar something, a sphere, far smaller than the Earth but taking up volume in three-dimensional space and surrounded by its own little electromagnetic field. However, as scientists probed deeper into the world of the very small, it became obvious that this view raised some difficulties. For example, our current understanding of physics tells us that there can be no such thing as a perfectly rigid body. Imagine striking a ball with a baseball bat. If the ball is perfectly rigid, it will go zooming off with no change of shape. However, in order for it to be able to do this, it means that all regions of the ball must begin moving simultaneously. Yet the region of the ball opposite the point of impact cannot possibly know about the blow at the exact same moment that the blow occurs, or information will have been conveyed without the passage of time—a violation of the speed-of-light limit. Only a shock wave can tell the region that one side of the ball has been struck by a bat. Hence, it is not possible for an object to be perfectly rigid without violating Einstein's theory of relativity.

It follows that if an electron is an object, even though very tiny, it must possess a certain amount of elasticity. However, if an electron is an elastic ball and can be squeezed into different shapes, it is implied that it can also be ripped apart, and we should expect to find an occasional bit or piece of an electron somewhere in the universe. Since this is not the case and no known process has ever resulted in the fragmentation of an electron, physics was forced to abandon the notion of an electron as a three-dimensional little sphere. Instead, the electron is now viewed as a structureless point, with no extension in three-dimensional space at all. This explanation solved one problem, but the notion of the electron as a structureless point brought with it another dilemma, and that is where renormalization comes in.

An electron is surrounded by a field of electrical energy. The energy of this field diminishes at a rate that is inversely proportional to the square of its distance from the center of the electron. (Centuries before physicists discovered this fact, Newton found that the same inverse-square law applies to the force of gravity.) Conversely, the force of the field surrounding the electron increases in strength the closer it is to the source. The problem is, with a point source possessing no extension in three-dimensional space, the strength of the field rises without limit. One cannot measure what lies up to the border of something that literally has no border. In other words, when measured, the total electrical energy of the field surrounding an electron appears to be infinite.

This is absurd, for if an electron actually possessed an infinite amount of energy, it would also be infinitely heavy. Since an electron is obviously not infinitely heavy, a way around the impasse had to be found. That way is renormalization. The presence of an infinite quantity in a calculation is often—but not always—a warning that something is wrong. If an infinite quantity shows up only in the mathematics describing a physical process and is never actually predicted by the mathematics to represent an observable quantity in the physical process, the presence of the infinite quantity in the calculation need not be viewed as necessarily troublesome. For example, imagine that an engineer is trying to design an apple-processing machine and, in the course of working out the mathematics of the design, arrives at the following equation:

5 apples in + an infinite number of apples =
5 apples out + an infinite number of apples

Obviously, the engineer will quickly realize that the two infinities cancel each other out, and what the equation is really telling him is that five apples in will equal five apples out. To streamline or "renormalize" the equation, all the engineer need do is remove the infinite quantity from either side of the equation. This is a crude analogy for how physicists dealt with the electron's apparently infinite cloak of energy. By reworking their equations, they found a way that the troubling infinities could be removed from the calculations. It was Glashow's genius to see how the infinite quantities in his own figures might be canceled out or *renormalized*.[2] However, despite Glashow's optimism, the theory that he arrived at in 1960 was ultimately found not to be renormalizable.[3]

Nonetheless, Glashow had reason to believe that he was on the right track, and he discovered two additional and unexpected propositions. The first was that another type of particle, in addition to the W, was predicted by the theory. This particle he called the Z. The second was that the W and the Z, as well as the photon, were all predicted to interact in a complicated way reminiscent of interactions described by gauge field theory.

Gauge field theory had been developed six years earlier by two American physicists, Chen Ning Yang and Robert Mills, for quite different purposes. Yang and Mills were exploring mathematical symmetries already developed by the mathematician Sophus Lie and known as Lie groups. Symmetry has to do with how objects change when we transform them. For example, if a sphere is rotated about an axis, it will remain unchanged. It can thus be said that the sphere has rotational symmetry about any axis. What Yang and Mills discovered, in particular, was that if one of the Lie group symmetries was imposed at a point in space, a new field was automatically required. This was intriguing, for it was the first time that it had been demonstrated that a symmetry mathematically required the existence of a field. Yang and Mills called their discovery gauge field theory, meaning that one could use a different "gauge" or measuring standard for each point in space.

In 1964, ignorant of Glashow's work, physicists Abdus Salam and J. C. Ward arrived at exactly the same theory of unification. What led Salam and Ward to their own conclusion was their long-held desire to explain all fundamental interactions as gauge field theory.

Gauge field symmetry seemed to imply that gauge fields had to be long range and to operate over great distances. Thus, gauge field theory seemed appropriate to apply to those forces that operated over great distances—electromagnetism and gravity. But no one yet knew how to describe those forces that operated only over microscopic distances—such as the strong and the weak nuclear forces—as gauge fields.

Then, in the early 1960s, Harvard's Steven Weinberg became interested in an idea that had originated earlier in solid-state physics and had been introduced to particle physics by a number of different theorists, including Heisenberg. This idea held that certain relations in quantum theory could possess very beautiful symmetries mathematically, but the symmetries might not be so neat. As Weinberg stated, "As theorists sometimes do, I fell in love with the idea." He began to wonder if different components of the gauge field might similarly appear as "spontaneously broken" when seen in the real world.[4]

An analogy for the concept of a "broken symmetry" can be drawn from the organic world. In almost all Earth life the double helix of DNA spirals toward the right. In other words, at first glance, nature seems to have built a "right-handedness" into the DNA molecule. However, in spite of the fact that no left-handed DNA has ever been found, there is no fundamental law of chemistry or physics dictating that this could never be the case. Presumably, the first self-replicating DNA molecule just happened to start spiraling toward the right and provided the prototype for all others to follow suit. Nonetheless, if a researcher had never seen a DNA molecule but, through mathematical and biochemical understanding, had predicted its existence, he or she would not be able to determine which preference—left-handedness or right-handedness—would ultimately manifest. In the mathematical description of the DNA molecule, there is perfect symmetry between the two preferences. It is only in physical reality that the symmetry is spontaneously broken, and "handedness," as it were, appears.

There seemed to be such alluring similarities between gauge field theory and the way natural forces interact that Weinberg started to explore intensively the possibility that some of the problems might be reconciled with the notion of broken symmetries. In 1967 he published the first mathematically coherent theory that unified the electromagnetic and weak nuclear force, and shortly thereafter, Salam announced his independent discovery of the same theory. According to the vision offered by Weinberg and Salam, nature had indeed patterned the interactions of her forces according to the beautiful symmetries of the gauge field theory. The fact that some forces can operate over long distances and others only over microscopic ones was an accident of fate, like the right-handedness of the DNA molecule. In the mathematical constructs describing physical reality, such symmetries were still extant. It was only in the arbitrary happenstance of physical reality that this ultimate symmetry was broken.[5]

Very little attention was initially paid to Weinberg's version of the theory. According to the 1967 *Science Citation Index,* not one of the other scientific papers published that year even made any reference to it. In 1968 the situation remained the same, as it did in 1969. Even in 1970 it was mentioned as a reference in only one other paper. As Sidney Coleman puts it, "Rarely has so great an accomplishment been so widely ignored." In 1971, 4 other published papers cited it as a reference. In 1972 the number had risen to 64; and in 1973 it was mentioned by 162 different published articles. Weinberg and Salam's "electroweak" theory was taking off.[6]

More and more researchers became interested in the new idea that all the forces of nature at least possessed a common description in terms of gauge fields. Then, in 1973, the existence of a new class of weak interactions predicted by the Weinberg–Salam theory, the so-called *neutral currents,* was confirmed experimentally. The theory received further support, starting in 1974, with the discovery of a whole new family of *hadrons,* a class of particles involved in the strong interactions. As the implications of the Weinberg–Salam theory dawned upon the scientific community, the successful unification of the weak and electromagnetic forces brought with it a growing feeling that still further unifications were possible. In 1973 Sheldon Glashow and Howard Georgi published a theory seeking to unify the electroweak force with the strong nuclear force. This was the first grand unified theory, or GUT, as it is now called. There are currently a number of contending GUTs, all based on the essential ideas advanced by Weinberg and Salam.

In 1972, as interest in the Weinberg–Salam theory started to accelerate, a second important discovery was made. Working at the Lebedev Physical Institute in Moscow, physicists D. A. Kirzhnits and A. D. Linde discovered that gauge field theories exhibit what is known as a *phase transition,* an abrupt transition from one state to another, much like the phase transition of water when it freezes and becomes ice. Kirzhnits and Linde discovered that at very high temperatures—temperatures above 3,000 trillion degrees ($3 \times 10^{15}$ degrees Kelvin)—the essential unity between the weak and the electromagnetic forces is still manifest, and the weak interactions obey the same sort of inverse square law as the electromagnetic interactions. It is only below this critical temperature that this unity "freezes" out. What is significant is that although no Earthly conditions can re-create such extremely high temperatures, it is believed that these were temperatures achieved only during the big bang. In other words, the symmetries that are now broken and hidden from us were once intact, but only during the very first moments of the creation.[7]

As cosmologists seized on this idea, it quickly became apparent that the Weinberg–Salam theory had important things to say about the origins of the universe itself. With the coming of the GUTs, it was proposed that at even higher temperatures—temperatures around $10^{28}$ degrees Kelvin—the strong force would also meld with the electromagnetic and the weak. Although no one has yet incorporated gravity in any grand unified theory, cosmologists are confident that a way will be found.[8] The current picture of the beginning of the universe is as follows: Out of a void in which there was not yet space or time, the universe ballooned into existence. For an instant all creation was a harmony of matter and energy, ruled by a single cosmic force, the superforce whence all of nature's forces derive. As the universe expanded, it cooled and fragmented like frost forming on a window. First gravity froze out, then the strong nuclear force, then the weak and the electromagnetic. As each new force broke away, the constituents of the early universe, quarks, gluons, neutrinos, and other exotic particles—once part of their own indistinguishable symmetry— separated and became trapped in the identities we recognize today.

It is significant to note that the universe we perceive today is only one of many possible universes that might have congealed out of the primordial flash of the superforce. Weinberg states: "As everyone knows, when water freezes it does not usually form a perfect crystal of ice, but something much more complicated: a great mess of crystal domains, separated by various types of crystal irregularities. Did the universe also freeze in domains? Do we live in one such domain, in which the symmetry between the weak and electromagnetic interactions has been broken in a particular way, and will we eventually discover other domains?"[9]

It is an interesting speculation. Equally interesting are some of the other propositions advanced by the GUTs. First among these is the prediction that the proton might be unstable and may ultimately decay. During the entire history of particle physics, one of the most inviolable rules has been that the proton is an absolutely stable particle. After all, protons are the cornerstone of the entire physical universe. If the proton is unstable and likely to decay, it means that matter itself will ultimately disintegrate and vanish— as Paul Davies observes in his recent book *Superforce,* "a very profound conclusion indeed."[10] For a number of years now, numerous groups have made extensive searches for a single example of this rare and freakish event, but none have met with any success.

Another very recent suggestion made by now so-called supersymmetry theories is that, instead of points, all of the basic particles may be composed of strings. String theories originated in the 1960s, but in 1984 physicist Michael Green of Queens College, University of London, and John H. Schwarz of the California Institute of Technology found a mathematical approach that has made string theories plausible enough to create a surge of interest. A special feature of superstring theories is that they depend on the exist of multiple dimensions beyond the four that apply to everyday life: length, width, height, and time. Numerous researchers around the world, including Edward Witten of Princeton, are currently working on combining superstring theories with supersymmetry theories. However, researchers caution that there is not yet any experimental evidence that indicates that such string theorists are on the right track.

Gregory Bateson once made the distinction between raw data, heuristic concepts, and fundamentals. As he stated, "Science investigators *think* advance is inductive—raw data lead to new heuristic concepts. These concepts are regarded as working hypotheses and tested against more data. Gradually, it is hoped, the heuristic concepts will be correlated and improved until at last they are worthy of a place in the list of fundamentals. About fifty years of work of which thousands of clever men have had their share have, in fact, provided a rich crop of several hundred heuristic concepts, but, alas, scarcely a single principle worthy of a place in the list of fundamentals."[11] In spite of the lack of success in finding any instances of proton decay, because of the mathematical elegance of the Glashow–Weinberg–Salam theory, many physicists began to believe that they had discovered a new scientific fundamental.

Nonetheless, as with any theory, the first step toward a new scientific fundamental lies in the finding of at least some corroborative experimental evidence.

# The Capture of the Elusive W

One of the predictions of the Glashow–Weinberg–Salam theory was the existence of a particle known as the W. In early 1983, a 134-member research team led by Italy's Carlo Rubbia of CERN announced that they had, indeed, found the W.

Glashow, Weinberg, and Salam were not the first researchers to suspect the existence of the W. Since the early decades of the century, quantum physics had established the understanding that a particle could be the carrier of a force. In fact, quantum theory requires that everything, including the force fields of nature, comes in discrete particles. In 1935 the Japanese physicist Hideki Yukawa published a paper asserting that the force binding together the particles in the atomic nucleus must therefore be carried by such a particle. In the same paper he also talked about a particle that might be responsible for carrying the weak force and predicted that the particle must be extremely shortlived and very massive.[1] Weinberg and Salam later proposed that actually three particles must carry the weak force, a positive and a negative W, and a neutral particle they called the Z, which was even more massive than the W, possessing ninety times the mass of the proton.

One of the problems in locating the W was its extremely high mass. The more massive the particle, the more energy that is required to produce it. Indeed, it was only with the recent development of very large accelerators that the finding of particles as massive as the W became a realistic possibility. Another problem was that billions of pieces of data had to be sifted through in order to find evidence of its existence. Some researchers likened finding the W to successfully finding a given person in a photograph of a billion people flashed quickly before one's eyes.

Undaunted, Rubbia believed that there were ways of finding the W. In spite of the fact that its lifetime is such a fraction of a second, the Glashow–Weinberg–Salam theory clearly spelled out what the elusive W would decay into; therefore, Rubbia knew that if he could not find the actual W, he could at least find the detritus of its existence. Nonetheless, even creating the W for just a fraction of a second required an amount of energy comparable to that previously reached in nature only during the first explosive seconds of the big bang.

Rubbia persuaded CERN to let him modify its major accelerator, the Super Proton Synchrotron, a four-mile circular atomic racetrack buried in a tunnel running far below the dairy farms and forests of the French–Swiss border. Rubbia altered the Super Proton Synchrotron so that, instead of sending a beam of protons in just one direction, it would shoot two sets of bullets—protons and their antimatter opposites, antiprotons—in opposite directions. Each beam would acquire an energy level of 270 billion electron volts; when they collided with each other, as a result of Rubbia's redesign, their collision energy would equal 540 billion electron volts. Rebuilding the accelerator took five years and $100 million.[2]

The first test occurred in 1981. Following that test, Rubbia succeeded in increasing the density of the particles in each beam, thereby increasing the number of collisions. According to theory, only about one W particle should be created during every one billion collisions. Nonetheless, in spite of the drastically increased amount of data, Rubbia and his team still managed to sift through the mountain of evidence and locate several additional instances of W particle disintegration. The Glashow–Weinberg–Salam theory gained momentum, but it wasn't until 1983, when Rubbia and his colleagues uncovered evidence of the Z, that the theory was clinched.

Rubbia's achievements have created a tremendous amount of excitement in the world of science. As Weinberg states, "It's really a watershed in experimental physics that these particles we've been talking about for so many years actually do exist. It is also tremendously gratifying for all of us theoreticians."[3]

The finding of the W and the Z has convinced most physicists that, in spite of remaining problems, the Glashow–Weinberg–Salam theory has brought science closer to the unification of nature's forces than ever before. As for what technological advances the unification of nature's four basic forces will bring, it is still too early to tell. The unification of just two of nature's forces, electricity and magnetism, paved the way for electric engines, X-rays, and telecommunications. It is safe to predict that the unification of all of nature's forces will certainly not bring with it any less.

Whatever else it brings, the finding of the W and the Z raises an often-repeated question among quantum physicists: Will there ever be an end to the number of particles we postulate and then discover in the subatomic landscape? The finding of the W and the Z is not the only recent event that raises this issue anew.

# Quarks and Demon Nuclei

For much of this century, physics has been distinguished by the discovery of a seemingly endless array of subatomic particles. In the late 1950s, partly because no one could believe that nature could be so maliciously complex, many theorists began to suspect that the jungle of particles they were observing was not the ultimate level of reality and that there remained an even simpler and as-yet-undiscovered class of building blocks. In 1963 Murray Gell-Mann formulated a mathematical model for these building blocks, dubbing them *quarks,* a word James Joyce had coined in *Finnegans Wake.* He proposed that there were three basic quarks from which a vast range of subatomic particles, such as protons and neutrons, were constructed, as well as three antiquark partners, antimatter versions of the three quarks with equal but opposite electric charges. His mathematical model was so simple and so elegant that physicists were convinced it was correct. They started looking for quarks in laboratory experiments, in cosmic rays, and in other places, but no one seemed to be able to find them. Whenever particles were split, physicists did not end up with quarks, just other already known particles.

Because Gell-Mann's model seemed so "right," physicists were reluctant to abandon it and concluded instead that, while quarks existed, for reasons curious and peculiar to the subatomic world, they could not be extracted from the particles they composed. In 1968 experimenters at Stanford University, using a two-mile-long linear electron accelerator, finally succeeded in demonstrating that a proton's electric charge was indeed concentrated in pointlike structures; and today, although most physicists concede that no one will ever see or observe a free quark, quarks have become a "reality."

After the Stanford discovery of quarks, some scientists started wondering if there might be more than three. In 1973 new theories of the interactions of quarks, based on elegant mathematical symmetries, started to persuade large numbers of physicists that there might indeed be extras. Like Gell-Mann's original concept, the new theories of guard interaction seemed so overwhelmingly right that it was difficult to ignore them. The only problem was that they did not work in experiments unless there was a fourth quark in the picture. In 1974, Sam Ting at Brookhaven National Laboratory and Burton Richter at Stanford simultaneously discovered the fourth quark. And so, in the words of Heinz Pagels, "The great quark hunt was on."[1]

Now, by the first half of the 1980s, physicists at Cornell University have announced that a fifth quark has been found.[2] The most recent models of quark behavior suggest that there also may be a sixth quark waiting in the wings, and some evidence of its existence has even been offered. Ironically, many physicists are starting to feel uncomfortable with such a large number of quarks. What started out as a path toward simplification may have turned out to be just another doorway into an uncharted subnuclear domain. Some treacherous questions are being asked: Are quarks themselves made out of more fundamental objects? Since quarks never occur as free, isolated particles, does it even make sense to talk

---

A chart of the different categories of quarks, the proposed building blocks of subatomic particles such as protons and neutrons. Scientists have found the fifth quark and believe that they may have found the sixth. The whimsical names serve to identify mathematical and measurable properties of each quark.

# A Quark Inventory

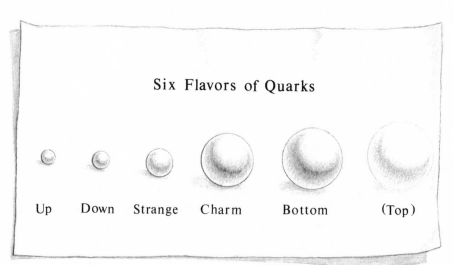

## Six Flavors of Quarks

Up    Down    Strange    Charm    Bottom    (Top)

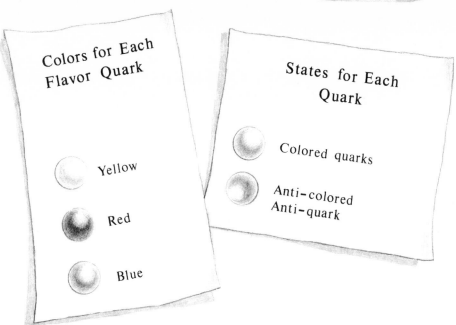

## Colors for Each Flavor Quark

Yellow

Red

Blue

## States for Each Quark

Colored quarks

Anti-colored Anti-quark

about their having parts? Pagels points out that "all present evidence supports this view that quarks are a 'rock bottom' to matter, but no physicist I know would be willing to bet much on that."[3]

Evidence has also recently been offered that quarks can come together to form new types of matter previously unknown to science. In 1980 E. M. Friedlander of the Lawrence Berkeley Laboratory reported that when high-energy nuclei collided with an emulsion target, they left markings on a photographic plate that could not be explained by any previously known particle. This suggested to Friedlander the existence of a new and unknown particle.[4] In 1982 S. Fredriksson and M. Jandl of the Royal Institute of Technology in Stockholm published a paper predicting, from a new theoretical approach, that the tracks might have been made by hitherto unexpected phenomenon, the grouping of quarks into *demon* nuclei—an exotic new type of matter in which individual protons and neutrons cannot be discerned.[5]

The six known or theorized quarks, believed to be the ultimate constituents of all matter, behave as if they possess a property called *color,* which is similar to an electrical charge. But instead of there being just one type of charge—a positive charge—quarks have three varieties of charge known as *red, yellow,* and *blue,* each of which has a positive and a negative state. Quarks carry positive colors, and antiquarks, their antimatter equivalent, carry the negative or complementary anticolors. As with electrical charges, unlike colors attract each other. Quarks and antiquarks are thus mutually attracted and form a variety of types of matter known as *mesons,* of which the *pion,* a relatively light particle first discovered coming down in cosmic rays, is the most familiar example.

However, because of the threefold nature of the quark's charge, quarks are able to cluster in ways that have no analogues in electromagnetism. For example, three different-color quarks—a red, a blue, and a yellow—can all come together and all attract one another, forming a particle known as a *baryon,* of which the neutron and the proton are the lightest examples. If a fourth quark comes

## Sample Hadrons (Made of Quarks)

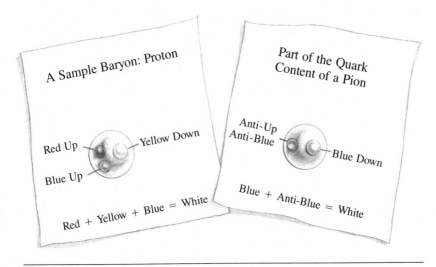

A Sample Baryon: Proton

Red Up — — Yellow Down

Blue Up

Red + Yellow + Blue = White

Part of the Quark Content of a Pion

Anti-Up
Anti-Blue — — Blue Down

Blue + Anti-Blue = White

Heavy particles such as protons and neutrons belong to a category of subatomic particles known as hadrons. All hadrons can in turn be divided into two further categories: mesons, or subatomic particles that possess whole-integer spins such as 0, 1, 2, and so on; and baryons, or subatomic particles that possess half-integer spins such as ½, ¾, and so on. The proton is a sample baryon, and the pion, a very light and unstable particle produced in certain nuclear reactions, is a sample meson. The actual pion is a mixture of each color plus its corresponding anti-color. Scientists now believe that the different properties in various hadrons are due to the different combinations of the quarks composing them.

near the ensemble, it will be repelled by its counterpart within the trio, making a baryon a very stable form for matter to be in.

As stated, an important distinction between quarks and electromagnetic forces is that individually colored quarks or pairs of quarks that carry a net color do not seem to be allowed by nature to have free existence. Quarks can exist only in clusters in which the net color of the entire cluster vanishes. For example, within the proton there exist two quarks, with a net color, attracted to a third quark that carries another color. In this sense, then, the proton can be viewed as a two-quark, or *di-quark,* colored ion (charged particle) connected to a quark colored ion. The question posed by Fredriksson and Jandl is, Can there be attractive forces between di-quarks within nuclear matter? For example, a familiar cluster of six would be a deuteron (an isotopic form of hydrogen) composed of two uncolored clusters of three quarks each, one a proton and the other a neutron. However, Fredriksson and Jandl's paper also raises the possibility that the deuteron might have a demon brother, one that has, instead of two uncolored clusters of three quarks each, three color ions of two quarks each—or a demon nucleus composed of three di-quarks.

Fredriksson and Jandl predict that such a particle would be light enough to be almost stable and thus might be responsible for the anomalous paths reported by Friedlander. However, shortly after the publication of their suggestion, H. J. Lipkin of the Weizmann Institute raised a powerful theoretical objection to the existence of such demon deuterons, arguing that whatever is responsible for Friedlander's experimental anomalies, it cannot be demon nuclei.[6] Thus, if demon nuclei do exist, it seems that they do not occur in the way that the Swedish group claim.

An intriguing lesson of the quark is its intrinsically paradoxical nature as a concept. Quarks are accepted as reality, but at the same time science admits that they can never be separated from the particles they are said to constitute. Perhaps in no other instance is the preeminence of *theory* over *reality,* the fact that the universe is at root a linguistic invention, better exemplified. The fact that the quark model has allowed physicists to continue to explore and to understand matter underscores a second important lesson inherent in Gell-Mann's quark theory. Admitting that the universe is an invention does not therefore make that invention any less useful as a tool. For, it is by and through inventing and re-inventing of the universe that we continue to manipulate the forces of nature in ways never previously thought possible.

That we have reached a point where reality and concept have become inseparable also suggests that the avalanche of particles we continue to discover will never come to an end. For, if we have reached the point where reality and concept are inseparable, we may surmise that the number of particles remaining to be discovered is limited only by our drive to invent. And as Gertrude Stein wrote, "Of course, you might say why not invent new names, new languages but that cannot be done. It takes a tremendous amount of inner necessity to invent even one word, one can invent imitating movements and emotions in sounds, and in the poetical language of some languages you can have that. . . . Language as a real thing is not imitation either of sounds or colors or emotions it is an intellectual recreation and there is no possible doubt about it and it is going to go on being that as long as humanity is anything.[7]

# *Part III*

## THE BIOLOGICAL UNIVERSE

S cience has known two revolutions in this century. The first was the revolution in physics in the form of Einstein's theory of relativity and quantum theory, both of which radically changed our understanding of the universe. The second revolution was in biology, in the deciphering of the DNA chain and the advent of molecular biology.

Unlike physics, which often deals with remote interstellar objects and minute and unseen particles, the world of biology sometimes seems more immediate and personal to us. Yet, not surprisingly, biological investigations are more and more enveloping the concerns of physics and astronomy.

This section presents a range of questions that include: What is the oncogene? Will science drastically increase our maximum life span? Does a death star periodically kill off most of the life on the Earth? What forms might life take on other planets? And how might genetic engineering allow us to redesign ourselves?

# The Death of the Dinosaurs

For over two centuries theories have been put forth, ranging from Noah's flood to the shifting of the Earth's poles, in attempts to explain the disappearance of the dinosaurs. Throughout all of the conjecture, one fact has remained certain. About 65 million years ago, something like 70 percent of all the animal species on the Earth vanished. A good portion of the planet life and even many one-celled creatures in the ocean vanished. A recent discovery has given us a substantial clue.

The discovery was made by a team of four investigators, including Walter Alvarez, professor of geology at the University of California at Berkeley; Alvarez's father, Luis W. Alvarez, of the Lawrence Radiation Laboratory at Berkeley and winner of the 1968 Nobel Prize in Physics for his work with elementary particles and the discovery of resonance states; and Frank Asaro and Helen V. Michel, two nuclear chemists from the same laboratory. The team, led by Walter Alvarez, was not initially looking for a clue to the death of the dinosaurs. What they were looking for was a better method for dating individual rock strata. They were employing a new analytical technique known as neutron activation analysis, or NAA, a process that made it possible to detect extremely small concentrations of various elements in soil samples.

Their search led them to Gubbio, a town of about thirty-two thousand in the Apennine mountains of central Italy. Since the sixteenth century, Gubbio has been known for its ceramics, and it was the clay from which these ceramics were made that drew the attention of Alvarez's team. What was special about the clay in Gubbio was that the strata dividing it into different geological periods were clearly delineated. By testing the chemical content of different strata, Alvarez and his group hoped to discover some peculiar chemical signature that would enable them to recognize immediately the age of similar strata in different parts of the world.

After unsuccessfully exploring several possibilities, the team set the sights of their NAA technique on iridium and osmium. Iridium and osmium are precious metals, precious because they are extremely rare. They both belong to a group of metals known as the *platinoids,* of which platinum is the most famous. Iridium and osmium are also known as *noble metals* because of their reluctance to combine chemically with other elements. The Alvarez team earmarked iridium and osmium as the focus of their study on account both of their rarity and of the relative ease with which they could be located using the NAA method. Finally, much of the iridium and osmium found on the Earth has drizzled down on us in the form of interstellar debris. By measuring the amount of these metals in the clay strata, the Alvarez team hoped to determine how long it had taken them to be deposited in the sediments.

On average, one may expect to find .006 parts of iridium for every million parts of rock in the Earth, and .0001 parts of osmium. However, when the Alvarez team reached the 65-million-year layer, they discovered over thirty times as much iridium as in the clay strata before and after and a similar jump in osmium.

This discovery raised an important question. Was the enrichment of the Gubbio clays purely a local event or might they find similar concentrations of iridium and osmium in strata at the same age at other locations around the world? The Alvarez team took samples of boundary clays first at a site about fifty kilometers south of Copenhagen and then from New Zealand's North Island, exactly on the other side of the world. The Danish samples were taken at a site near Hojerup Church at Stevns Klint, famous for its "fish clays"—so called because of the many fossilized fish in them. The New Zealand samples were taken from a site near Woodside Creek, about forty kilometers northeast of Wellington. The team found that at the 65-million-year mark, the New Zealand sample contained about 20 times more iridium than in clay boundaries before or after. The Danish samples contained 160 times the average level. Continued tests revealed that it was not only iridium and osmium that were present in such concentrated levels but many other unusual metals as well. It was as if nature had somehow wreaked havoc on the chemistry of the clay at those levels. Alvarez and his team published their results in 1979 in the *Geological Society of America, Abstracts with Program*.[1]

As usually happens when an exciting new anomaly emerges in science, other researchers quickly started checking the Alvarez findings. In doing so, they found themselves adding more supportive data from many new sites. Unusual concentrations of iridium were found in the same clay boundary in Zumaya, in northern Spain, and in Caravaca, in southern Spain; at El Kef in northern Tunisia; and even in core samples brought up from the floor of the Pacific Ocean by researchers on the United States research ship *Glomar Challenger*.

Researchers J. Smit of the Geological Institute in Amsterdam and J. Hertogen of Belgium traveled to Caravaca, Spain, and collected several hundred samples at different levels of the clay. In a thorough search, they tested for the presence of twenty-seven different elements. What they found was that, although the elements occurred in expected concentrations through most of the layers, in the clay boundary in question concentrations of iridium were 450 times the average, osmium 250 times, and arsenic 110 times. Chromium was 9 times richer than the average concentration, cobalt 30 times richer, nickel 44 times richer, selenium 40 times richer, and tin 20 times richer. Smit and Hertogen also observed that, precisely at the testing level, the number of fossils present diminished greatly. It was this clay boundary that divided the Cretaceous period, the age of the dinosaurs, from the Tertiary. Might it be more than coincidence that the unusual concentrations occurred at exactly the strata when the dinosaur apparently vanished?[2]

This thought had already crossed the minds of the Alvarez group. In the June 1980 issue of *Science,* they argued that it was extremely unlikely that the concentrations had arisen from local phenomena. It would simply be too much of a coincidence to find the same concentrations taking place at the same time in so many different locations. The Alvarez team suggested that the iridium must have come from space. Smit and Hertogen took a similar view, arguing that interstellar materials are often high in iridium and osmium and that only some sort of extraterrestrial impact could account for their high concentration in the clay boundary.[3] Slowly, other scientists began to agree that the evidence was most compelling and that an extraterrestrial source seemed the most likely explanation.

If, then, the metals came from space, in what sort of form did they arrive? Four possible answers were considered: from a cloud caused by a supernova explosion; from a dust cloud; from a comet; or from a meteorite. If the metals had come from a supernova explosion, osmium could be used to test the hypothesis. Osmium is found on the Earth in two isotopic forms with slightly different atomic weights, osmium 184 and osmium 190. The proportionate relationship of these two osmiums is stable throughout the planet and presumably throughout the Solar System; their ratio is a reflection of the original osmium content of the primordial dust cloud from which both the Earth and the Solar System formed. In the current view, all the heavier elements in the universe are by-products of the fusion processes of heavier stars, and relatively young star systems such as our own are formed out of interstellar clouds ejected by supernova explosions. Hence, if the osmium present in the clay boundary had come from a different supernova explosion than the supernova explosion from which our Solar System was formed, it would be extremely unlikely that its isotopes would be found in the same proportions they usually have on our planet. So, the proportions of the two osmium isotopes in the strata were measured, and they were found to be the same as those present throughout the Earth and also in meteoric material from within the Solar System. This finding seemed to rule out the possibility that the osmium had come from a different supernova source.[4]

What, then, about the interstellar dust cloud hypothesis? Frank T. Kyte, Zhiming Zhou, and John T. Wasson of the Institute of Geophysics and Planetary Physics of the University of California at Los Angeles calculated that, to deliver the requisite amount of iridium, the dust cloud would have to have had a diameter of about 860 trillion kilometers—ten times larger than the largest known dust clouds in our neighborhood of the galaxy. In addition, Kyte's group pointed out that the iridium was concentrated in such a narrow band in the clay boundary that, to be able to deposit it in such locations as the bottom of the ocean, the cloud would have to have been ten times denser than what was allowed in their original calculations. These findings made the explanation of a dust cloud extremely unlikely.[5]

That left the possibility of deposit by a comet or by a meteorite. In an article in a 1980 issue of *Nature,* Kenneth J. Hsu of the Geological Institute of Technology at Zurich favored the comet explanation. Hsu calculated that the comet would have to have been about the size of Halley's comet, or about a trillion tons. Given that hydrogen and methyl cyanide have been detected in the tail of the comet Kohoutek, Hsu went on to suggest that perhaps it was the cyanides in the comet that actually killed off much of the life on the Earth 65 million years ago.[6] However, as Kyte's group pointed out later, it is doubtful that cyanides could survive the temperatures incurred when the comet passed through the Earth's atmosphere. Kyte's group was convinced that such cyanides would be oxidized and become harmless.[7] Other investigators have also argued that even if cyanides did enter the Earth's oceans, they would not have dispersed far from the point of impact and would still not explain the death of animals at far points of the globe.

The Alvarez group itself favored the meteorite explanation. According to their calculations, if a meteorite of about 7.5 kilometers in diameter hit the Earth, whether on the land or in the oceans, its impact would have sent up a dust cloud sufficient to explain the iridium concentration present in the clay boundaries. They theorized that such an impact could spew high into the Earth's atmosphere, causing a temporary absence of sunlight that would effectively shut off photosynthesis and, in turn, adversely affect all life forms on the Earth. They stated: "The food chain in the open ocean is based on microscopic floating plants, such as the coccolith-producing algae, which show a nearly complete extinction. The animals at successively higher levels in this food chain were also very strongly affected, with nearly total extinction of the foraminifera and complete disappearance of the belemnites, ammonites, and marine reptiles. A second food chain is based on land plants. Among these plants, existing individuals would die, or at least stop producing new growth, during an interval of darkness, but after light returned they would regenerate from seeds, spores, and existing root systems. However, the large herbivorous and carnivorous animals that were directly or indirectly dependent on this vegetation would become extinct."[8]

Such an impact would have produced a great deal of heat, and evidence of this great heat has been found. Searching for further evidence, Smit and another colleague, G. Klaver, also of the Geological Institute in Amsterdam, returned to Caravaca, Spain. On this trip they discovered many small spherules of a glassy material in the clay boundary in question. Such spherules are sometimes found in the vicinity of volcanic activity, although Smit reports that a chemical analysis of the Caravaca spherules shows them to have a chemical composition inconsistent with those of volcanic origin.[9]

Not all researchers agree with the extraterrestrial impact theory. According to geologist Dewey McLean of the Virginia Polytechnic Institute, the iridium layer could be explained by tremendous volcanic activity that might have occurred in India during the Cretaceous–Tertiary transition time. As he sees it, an unusually large outpouring of lava would have released tremendous amounts of carbon dioxide. If the atmosphere became sufficiently saturated, the gas would have diffused into the waters of the ocean, increasing their acidity and thus destroying calcareous algae, plankton. Massive death of plankton would have meant a halt to the regular deposit of dead calcareous plankton on the ocean's floor. In the absence of such a regular fall, McLean feels that the normal drizzle of iridium that rains down on the Earth every day could have accumulated in an unusual layer, thus forming the clay boundary in question.

In turn, the loss of plankton, which usually consumes carbon dioxide in the atmosphere, would have resulted in greater and greater accumulations of the gas. Such a saturation of carbon dioxide in the atmosphere would have created a geenhouse effect, thus increasing the temperature on the Earth by as much as several degrees. As McLean points out, since dinosaurs had a volume disproportionately greater than the surface area of their bodies, a temperature increase of even a few degrees would have been devastating to them.[10]

A surprising number of scientists have aligned themselves behind the extraterrestrial explanation. In their 1983 book *The Great Extinction,* science writer Michael Allaby and physicist James Lovelock state, "The evidence thus far is circumstantial. But so is a smoking gun. The verdict of the scientific jury, returned in late 1980, was that these species had died suddenly under circumstances that suggested an extraterrestrial origin."[11]

Leo Hickey, a paleobotanist at the Smithsonian, finds fault with the notion that the extinction of so much of the life on the Earth was due to a dust cloud blocking out the Sun. On the basis of the fossil record of plants in Montana, Wyoming, and Alberta, Canada, he argues that the dinosaurs may have become extinct at least tens of thousands of years before the big turnover in plants. He also estimates that, during an interval of about 2 million years, at least 50 percent of all plant species survived, many more than the asteroid theory seems to allow for.

He points out that the apparent geographic distribution of the plant extinction seems to rule out the idea that they starved to death because a dust cloud deprived them of sunlight. Although a dust cloud could lead to the extinction of all the adult plants of a species, the species would not necessarily die out, because it could regenerate from seeds. In temperate areas seeds may lie dormant for many years. However, in tropical areas, "seed dormancy is on the average much shorter, on the order of months or weeks or in some cases even days."[12] The problem, as Hickey points out, is that the evidence is exactly the opposite. Many tropical floras appear to have remained untouched, while in certain temperate regions the extinction rate was as high as 90 percent. As for the cause of the extinction, Hickey states, "I'd love for it to have been a catastrophe because it would make things simpler. But my work doesn't show it. It looks like there is something to the asteroid hypothesis, but the damage [that it proposes] looks too great."[13]

Walter Alvarez has responded to Hickey's assertion. He holds that "plants are not really a sensitive indicator." Although Hickey's view argues against the notion of a Sun-shielding cloud enveloping the Earth for several years, Alvarez proposes that it does not argue against a cloud having blocked out the Sun for a few months.

Allaby and Lovelock also feel that a prolonged period of darkness is feasible, but add that some of the damage to plant life might also have occurred because the dust coated the leaves of plants. They feel that volcanic activity most certainly would have followed the impact and point to the fact that, after Mount St. Helens in Washington State erupted, dust coated the leaves of plants up to 250 miles away, thickly enough to prevent photosynthesis.

Allaby and Lovelock, like other researchers before them, propose that the most likely point of impact is in one of the Earth's oceans. This would explain why there is no apparent evidence of the estimated 175-kilometer-wide crater that would have been left by such an impact. If such an impact had occurred, the heat generated would have raised the temperature of the Earth's oceans at the time. Allaby and Lovelock report that evidence for such an increase exists.

From studying the isotopes of oxygen in core samples taken from the Pacific seabed by the Deep Sea Drilling Project, it has been determined that, at the very end of the Cretaceous period, the temperature of the seabed and the surface waters increased abruptly by between 1 and 5 degrees Celsius. No evidence exists for a general change in climate to account for such a transition, and the evidence of the core samples also indicates that it was shortlived.[14]

The American astronomer Fred L. Whipple of the Smithsonian Astrophysical Observatory at Cambridge, Massachusetts, points out that an extraterrestrial object 10 kilometers in diameter enter-

---

What caused the death of the dinosaurs has long been one of the most outstanding biological mysteries of all time. Recently, evidence has come forth that periodic collisions between the Earth and showers of asteroids or comets may have been responsible. Because the evidence suggests that such collisions take place roughly once every 26 million years, some scientists have proposed that the Sun might have a hitherto unsuspected stellar companion with a greatly elongated orbit, a hypothetical death star dubbed "Nemesis." According to this view, as Nemesis passes by the Solar System once every 26 million years, it disturbs the Oort cloud, a ring of dust and debris surrounding the Solar System, which in turn sends a periodic rain of comets down upon the Earth.

ing the North Atlantic at 20 kilometers per second would puncture the oceanic crust, making a hole about 100 kilometers in diameter, and would very likely have triggered intense volcanic activity. Whipple believes that evidence of such volcanic activity exists. He feels that the impact site may have been on or very close to the mid-oceanic ridge and that the actvity in the Earth's crust it triggered led to the emergence of Iceland. He cites as evidence that Iceland sits squarely on top of the mid-oceanic ridge, on top of a linear volcano that produces geysers, hot springs, and boiling mud. It is also a fact that Iceland continues to grow—the emergence of the island of Surtsey off its coast some twenty years ago proved that to a startled world. Last but not least, no rocks more than 65 million years old have ever been found on Iceland. Whether or not the impact of that fateful meteorite actually created Iceland is still in doubt, but it is a fact that Iceland emerged from the sea following a large volcanic eruption about 65 million years ago.[15]

Says Alvarez, "Among the many implications of the asteriod impact hypothesis, if it is correct, [one stands] out prominently. If the C–T (Cretaceous–Tertiary) extinctions were caused by an impact event, the same could be true of the earlier major extinctions as well. There have been five such extinctions since the Precambrian 570 million years ago, which matches well the probable interval of about 100 million years between collisions with 10-kilometer-diameter objects."[16]

Other scientists have agreed. In 1983 two paleontologists from the University of Chicago, David Raup and John Sepkoski, made a discovery that has set off a debate as heated as the one that followed the Alvarez group's discovery. After running a careful computer analysis of fossil records of the decline and extinction of families of marine animals over the past 250 million years, they concluded that the numerous large-scale extinctions that swept the Earth occurred in apparently regular cycles, about once every 26 million years.[17]

Raup and Sepkoski's revelation had an electric effect on many scientists. Although some criticized their findings on the grounds that the fossil record is blurry and that it is difficult to assess accurately the precise date of the extinction of any given species, because of the meticulousness of their methods and the prevailing intellectual climate in favor of catastrophism, numerous other scientists were receptive and even thrilled by their discovery. Taking up the gauntlet, some noted that if mass extinctions were cyclic rather than random, they must have had a common cause. Naturally, this assumption leads to the question, What could it be? Because no terrestrial phenomenon is known that could explain the 26-million-year cycle, researchers have again turned to the heavens for an answer.

Michael R. Rampino of Columbia University and Richard B. Strothers of the Goddard Institute of Space Studies note that the periods are strongly suggestive of the time it takes the Solar System to oscillate vertically about the plane of the Galaxy. They suggest that perhaps every 26 million years or so the oscillation of the Solar system through the galactic plane disrupts the Oort cloud, a vast bubble of comets that scientists believe surrounds the Solar System at a distance of up to 10 trillion miles from the Sun. Like a huge comb pulling fruit from a tree, the gravitational pull of the dust in the galactic plane might rake showers of comets out of the Oort cloud and send them hurtling through the Solar System, colliding with planets such as the Earth.[18] Richard D. Schwartz and Philip B. James of the University of Missouri agree and also see a correlation between the cycle and the Sun's oscillation about the galactic plane.[19]

An even more intriguing theory, and one that is gaining increasing scientific support and popular attention, is Richard Muller's so-called *death star* hypothesis. A physicist at Lawrence Berkeley Laboratory, Muller points out that many stars in the galaxy are part of double star systems in which both members orbit a common center of gravity. Perhaps, Muller and his group suggested, the Sun has a dim, undiscovered companion, a death star they dub

*Nemesis,* with an orbit that brings it close to the Solar System every 26 million years. As the star draws close, its gravitational pull would also disturb the Oort cloud, causing abnormal numbers of comets to come spilling out, resulting in the bombardment of the Earth and mass extinctions. The same hypothesis has also been put forth by Daniel Whitmire of the University of Southwestern Louisiana and Albert Jackson of Computer Sciences Corporation in Houston.[20]

If Nemesis exists astronomers suggest that it may be a red dwarf with an orbit that takes it at least two light-years out into space and then brings it back to about half a light-year away—near enough to disturb the inner Oort Cloud.

Although Whitmire has not ruled out the death star hypothesis, he has offered another possibility as well. Since the nineteenth century astronomers have noticed discrepancies in the movements of Neptune and Uranus that seem to indicate the existence of an as-yet-undiscovered planet in the Solar System. Even the discovery of Pluto in 1930 did not provide the gravitational force needed to justify Uranus's erratic behavior, and some astronomers continue to believe that there is a tenth planet somewhere out there. Whitmire and fellow Louisiana astrophysicist John Matese believe that the existence of such a planet might explain both the discrepancies in Uranus's orbit and the periodic showers of comets on the Earth. According to their calculations, Planet X, as they call it, would have to have an enormously elongated orbit that would bring it near the Oort cloud only once every 28 million years or so. It would also have to have a mass one to five times that of the Earth's.

Muller, a longtime colleague of Alvarez, has considered both the galactic oscillation and Planet X theories, but still believes that the Nemesis hypothesis presents the fewest problems. Whatever the correct view, all sides conceded that the only convincing proof will come with further observational evidence. In this regard numerous groups are already scanning the heavens, some looking for Nemesis and others looking for Planet X. Even if they do find one or the other, researchers note that if the calculations are correct, neither Nemesis nor Planet X is due to sweep past the Earth again for another 15 million years.

In spite of this fact, the discovery of either Nemesis or Planet X could still have a radical effect on our image of ourselves and of life on Earth in general. For example, if the Earth is visited by cyclic catastrophic impacts, such a discovery could shake the foundations of evolutionary biology and gravely call into question our current ideas about natural selection. If the planetary-impact theory is correct, says Harvard paleontologist Stephen Jay Gould, the importance of competition between the species would be greatly reduced. Planetary impact, not Darwinian survival of the fittest, might be the reason that mammals wrenched the Earth from the dinosaurs. Were it not for such a catastrophe, reptiles might have evolved as the most intelligent life form on the planet.[21]

# Is Darwin Evolving?

Charles Darwin died a little over a hundred years ago, on April 19, 1882, but many of the questions raised by his book *On the Origin of Species by Means of Natural Selection* are still being debated today. These issues include: How fast do new evolutionary advances in a species assert themselves? How related are we to other species? How and why does evolutionary change take place? What role does the complexity of the DNA chain play in these processes? The answers to these questions will not only tell us more about ourselves, about where we came from and where we are going, but may also spark breakthroughs in other fields, such as genetic engineering, plant science, and medicine. Although most scientists agree with the fundamental notions of evolutionary theory, there is a wide variance of opinion on many of the particulars of Darwin's ideas. A number of recent events have added to the century-old debate.

For the past forty years the study of evolutionary biology has been dominated by the *Modern Synthesis,* a term coined by Julian Huxley in 1942. The Modern Synthesis was the result of a marriage between Darwinism and a Mendelian understanding of genetics. The two major postulates of the Modern Synthesis can be summarized as follows: First, genetic mutation is the source of variability in organisms, and the resulting shift in gene frequencies that may arise is the source of evolutionary change. The origin of species and the development of trends in groups of species are explained as a result of the gradual accumulation of these small genetic differences. According to this understanding, the pace of evolutionary change is gradual, small changes accumulating over periods of many millions of years, causing animals to evolve steadily through time. The classical example of this trend is the evolution of the modern-day horse. The early ancestor of the horse, *Eohippus,* was a three-toed creature about the size of a dog. True to the assertions of the Modern Synthesis, the fossil record clearly reveals a slow and steady evolution in body size and form until *Eohippus* becomes the familiar *Equus.*

Secondly, the direction of evolutionary change is molded and determined by natural selection. That is, genetic mutations that allow organisms to adapt more successfully to their environments tend to survive and to be passed on to offspring; and genetic mutations that result in less successful adaptations tend to be quickly eliminated.

The current controversy in evolutionary theory centers around three major issues: the tempo of evolutionary change; the mechanisms of evolutionary change; and the constraints on the physical form, or morphology, of new organisms.

The problem, and one of the reasons for the current controversy, is that the gradual and steady evolution of *Eohippus* to *Equus* is only one type of evolution apparent in the fossil record. Paleontologists point out that it is also common to find fossil evidence of species that remain unchanged for millions of years and then abruptly vanish, to be replaced by substantially different versions of the former species. In fact, the absence of transitional forms between established species is so widespread that even Darwin himself commented on it and suggested that it was due to imperfections in the fossil record. As he saw it, the accumulation of sediments and the entrapment and fossilization of animals was, at best, a capricious process, and there were bound to be gaps in the record. However, at a 1980 conference on evolutionary biology held at Chicago's Field Museum of Natural History, a number of

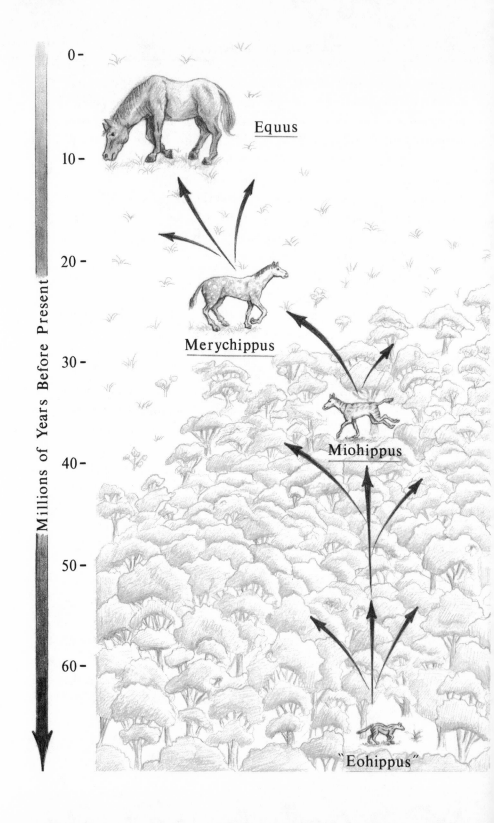

Millions of Years Before Present

0 —

10 —

Equus

20 —

Merychippus

30 —

Miohippus

40 —

50 —

60 —

"Eohippus"

researchers—ranging from geologists and paleontologists to embryologists, molecular biologists, population geneticists, and ecologists—discussed in earnest a view that has been gaining momentum over the years. The gaps may not be just imperfections in the fossil record but may point to an important and previously ignored aspect of evolution.

In the November 1980 issue of *Science,* Roger Lewin summarizes some of the new views prevailing among evolutionary theorists. He reports that Steven Stanley of Johns Hopkins University argued, "The record is not so woefully incomplete, you can reconstruct long sections by combining data from several areas." Stephen Jay Gould echoes the sentiment, stating, "Certainly the record is poor, but the jerkiness you see is not the result of gaps; it is the consequence of the jerky mode of evolutionary change."[1]

Lewin goes on to say that there was a great deal of debate on this point at the conference until Anthony Hallam of Birmingham University, England, came forward with a blackboard sketch of the paleontological history of Jurassic bivalves demonstrating the importance of stasis or long periods of stability in evolution. Then the mood at the conference began to change perceptibly in favor of recognizing stasis as a real phenomenon. Even some of the founders of the Modern Synthesis, such as Francisco Ayala, were persuaded that stasis was a newly understood feature of macroevolution. Stated Ayala, "We would not have predicted stasis from population genetics, but I am now convinced from what the paleontologists say that small changes do not accumulate."[2]

The current picture of evolutionary change that is emerging is one of long periods during which individual species remain virtually unchanged, punctuated by abrupt events after which a descendant species arises from the original stock. This new

---

Although scientists no longer believe that the evolution of the horse was as smooth or as continuous as depicted in this diagram, the evolution of the horse was long cited as the classical example of Darwinian evolution.

view—although Lewin points out that it was originally put forth in the 1930s in the "much maligned writings of Richard Gold-schmidt"—is known as *punctuated equilibrium,* and its most articulate proponents are Stephen Jay Gould of Harvard and Niles Eldredge of the American Museum of Natural History, New York.

Given the growing consensus in favor of punctuated equilibrium, what becomes of the linear morphological trends seen in some species, such as the evolution of *Eohippus* into modern-day *Equus?* The explanation offered by Gould and Eldredge is that the evolution of the horse can be viewed as a differentially pruned bush rather than a directed ladder. The horse has evolved in numerous directions, but those that have proved less advantageous to adaptation are eliminated. Those branches of the bush are pruned, making it lean steadily toward a single apparent direction.

In a classical Darwinian view, external events determine which branches get pruned and which do not. Elizabeth Vrba of the Transvaal Museum, Pretoria, has sought to refine Gould's and Eldredge's notion even further, by postulating that internal parameters may be the important determinant of the rates of speciation and extinction. To back up her argument, she calls attention to two groups of antelope, the *Alcelaphini* (wildebeests, hartebeests, etc.), which are highly specialized in the food they eat and the habitats they can occupy, and the *Aepycerotini* (impalas), which are generalists and can survive in a wide range of habitats and on a wide range of foods. As Vrba points out, the fossil record shows just two or three species of *Aepycerotini* (the generalists) over a period of 6 million years, whereas there are at least twenty-seven species of *Alcelaphini* (the specialists) over the same timespan. Vrba explains that specialists occupy very narrow biological ruts and can therefore tolerate many related species in their habitat in similar but distinct narrow ruts. Thus, new species can branch off or "speciate" from them frequently. However, being specialists, they are also particularly vulnerable to extinction because relatively small

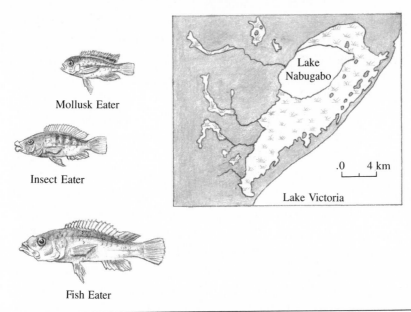

Mollusk Eater

Insect Eater

Fish Eater

Scientists believe that Lake Nabugabo separated from Lake Victoria only about 4,000 to 5,000 years ago. However, the three fish illustrated in the diagram, which are native to Lake Victoria, all have counterparts in Lake Nabugabo that are similar but have evolved into different species. Theorists suggest that this is evidence that the creation of a new species of higher organisms does not necessarily take millions of years, as proposed in the classical Darwinian view, but may occur over relatively short periods of time.

changes in environment can wipe out their narrow ecological niche. Conversely, generalists do not occupy such a narrow rut and are much more intolerant of related species occupying their territory. As a result, they do not speciate frequently but, being generalists, are also less susceptible to extinction.

Vrba concludes that the evolutionay history of a group of related species, such as antelopes, that display a spectrum of survival strategies from specialization to generalism can be sketched as a skewed branching bush leaning heavily toward the rapid speciators. Consequently, whatever morphological features characterize the rapid speciators will appear in the fossil record as evolutionary trends. Vrba calls this the *effect hypothesis.*

If stasis is accepted as a far more common state than was previously thought, it is also not without its problems. For example, it is now common knowledge that the fruit fly *Drosophila* and, presumably, other organisms can undergo genetic mutation quite readily. This being the case, how can paleontologists suggest that species remain the same through most of their existence? Similarly, given the apparent plasticity of the genetic makeup of such organisms, what could possibly explain the fact that after long periods of stability, speciation can occur in an instant? In answer to this, Gould first points out that what appears to be an instant in the fossil record is really quite a vast tract of time. A period of fifty thousand years between successive samples followed up a column of rock would be regarded as an extraordinarily continuous fossil record by most paleontologists. If the minimum "instant" apparent in the fossil record is roughly fifty thousand years, there is more than enough time for speciation to occur. The peppered moth, *Biston betularia,* was able to change from light to dark to camouflage itself in less than a hundred years after the industrial revolution started to pollute its habitat with vast quantities of soot.

As for the fact that species seem to undergo only minor modifications in spite of the apparent frequency of genetic mutation, Gould believes that such mutations are merely oscillations about a mean. Biologist Brian Charlesworth of Sussex University sees the matter in a similar way and asserts that natural selection actually functions to preserve the status quo rather than to promote change. He holds that it is not difficult to accept that many morphological features of various species have a sort of optimal value that would tend to make such features stable over long periods of time. For example, human babies all tend to be around the same average birth weight because babies that are too heavy and babies that are too light simply don't survive as well. In this light, Charlesworth believes that a sort of stabilizing selection comes into play.

Charlesworth does not believe the formation of new species is a special class of evolutionary event. He feels that Gould's ideas do not point out any new phenomena and that stasis is quite consistent with Darwin's original understandings.[3]

As for the second area of contention, the mechanisms of evolutionary change, there have been a number of new discoveries in the field of molecular biology. Primary among these is a growing understanding of the specific functions of certain coded sequences in the DNA chain, in particular, the sequences that code for proteins.

It has been discovered that the sequences that code for proteins make up only a very small portion of the entire DNA chain. For example, in the human genome—the package of genetic material that is passed from parent to progeny—only slightly more than 1 percent of the DNA chain is composed of protein-coding genes. No one is sure about what much of the rest of the genome does. All that can be said at the moment is that the remaining genetic material falls into three vague classes. About 5 percent is made up of a large family of short and simple repeats of nucleotide sequences known as *satellite DNA*. A quarter is formed of families of longer and more complex repeat sequences, denoted *intermediate repetitive DNA,* and the remaining bulk of the genome is composed of a unique sequence of *single copy DNA* interspersed with the intermediate repeats. The proportions of these classes vary between organisms, and the distinctions between them in any given organism can often be blurred.

This presents a puzzle. If only a small proportion of the genome provides the blueprint for the entire range of protein molecules in living organisms, what does the remaining genetic material do? For a number of years biologists were persuaded that it might be "junk" and that for some reason it was tolerated in the nuclei of higher organisms. Then, in 1980, a brace of papers appeared in *Nature* in which Ford Doolittle and Carmen Sapienza of Dalhousie University, Nova Scotia, and Leslie Orgel and Francis Crick of the Salk Institute, California, advanced the notion that much of the noncoding DNA might be *selfish DNA,* or DNA that had become a sort of parasitic passenger in the nuclei of higher organisms and whose sole purpose in existence was to replicate itself.

This premise was debated at a conference of molecular and evolutionary biologists held in 1981 at King's College, Cambridge. Some, such as Britain's foremost evolutionary theorist, John Maynard Smith, agreed that much of the genome might be selfish DNA.[4] Others, such as Gabriel Dover of the Genetics Department, Cambridge, argued that the proportion of selfish DNA was actually small, but conceded that studies of families of repeated sequences indicated that the DNA is passively and accidentally multiplied by a variety of mechanisms. He therefore asserted that the DNA should be referred to as *ignorant* as opposed to *selfish.*[5] Above and beyond all this semantic give-and-take, at least one unified message came through: Whatever the genomic DNA was, it was in a dynamic state. The question thus became, How important is it to the function of the organism?

Maynard Smith observed that it was very likely that it had some effect on the host organism. He suggested that it might be involved in some sort of signaling process between sequences, or at the very least—because it increased the amount of DNA in the nucleus—it might influence the size and reproductive time of the host cells.[6] Roy Britten and Eric Davidson of the California Institute of Technology feel it does far more than that. They have evidence that the sequences play an important role in moving genes in and out of regulatory positions. To support their claim, Davidson calls attention to the fact that the code for specific proteins is found in different positions in the genome of different organisms. As he puts it, "Old genes in new contexts give new morphology."[7]

The notion that there are movable elements in the DNA sequence or so-called *jumping genes* is not new. It is one of the ironies of science that it was actually discovered over thirty years ago. In the 1940s geneticist Barbara McClintock at the Cold Spring Harbor Laboratory in New York discovered that there was a whole class of mutant genes in maize *(Zea mays)* in which pigmentation had reverted to the wild-type (natural) red color in patches on some of the seeds. She noted that this result was similar to one reported by her colleague, the cytogeneticist Marcus Rhoades, who had discovered that homozygous black corn—so-called because the genes for color are identical in both parental chromosomes—which should have produced only black progeny actually gave rise to black with a few dotted and colorless seeds. McClintock studied the matter further and became convinced that, indeed, there was some sort of "controlling element" involved in making the readjustment. It should be noted that this was long before anyone knew about double helixes and genetic codes.

McClintock published her findings and then proceeded to demonstrate that the controlling element shifted about from one generation to the next, and when it moved, it brought a different structural gene under its control. McClintock even suggested that the physical rearrangements of the DNA might be the basis for the jumping gene's expression, but her work was considered controversial and even mystical.

McClintock continued in her work, an intellectual in exile for three decades, until James Shapiro, professor of microbiology at the University of Chicago, clearly demonstrated the existence of jumping genes in bacteria. Many questions remain to be answered about jumping genes—how they know how to operate; whether they make evolutionary leaps, etc.—but the importance of McClintock's work has now been recognized. In October 1983 she was awarded a Nobel Prize for her discovery.

Researchers continue to be troubled by the notion that the remaining noncoded sequences in the genome are junk. Alec Jeffreys of Leicester University notes that the structural genes with the most closely charted evolutionary history are those coded for globin, the protein component of hemoglobin. In studying the structure of globin clusters in a wide range of organisms, it has been possible to reconstruct the evolutionary path of a single globin gene of some 500 million years ago to the highly evolved arrangements of the molecule found in humans. What is interesting is that the five globin genes in the cluster in humans are interspersed over vast stretches of the troubling noncoded sequences of DNA. Jeffreys set out to analyze this DNA sequence in detail throughout the primate order and found that the single copy and repeated sequences that make up the region are strongly conserved. As he states, "We had set out to test the junk hypothesis and we were happy to rule it out provisionally in that these sequences have behaved in evolution as if they are functional." What this function is, Jeffreys confesses, remains to be determined.[8]

A subplot in the story of globin gene evolution is that a protein called leghemoglobin, which is involved in nitrogen fixation, has been discovered in legumes. The leghemoglobin molecule has all the appearances of a primitive globin gene. Jeffreys suggests that the most obvious explanation for the presence of an animal gene in the genome of a plant is that it was translocated there as a passenger on a virus relatively recently in evolution. The possibility that genes might be transmitted horizontally between different species is a new concept and is also causing growing interest among researchers. Such horizontally traveling genes could, theoretically, completely circumvent the classic Mendelian rules of inheritance.[9]

Up until now, evolutionists have recognized only two processes that could spread mutations of genes to all individuals in a population and so create evolutionary change. The first and foremost is natural selection. More recently population geneticists have recognized a second evolutionary force called "genetic drift," or the random genetic changes that seem to drift through small or isolated populations. For example, populations of Hawaiian land snails display a remarkable range of diversity in the coloring and shapes of their shells. Evolutionists can find no definable differences in environmental factors that might account for such seemingly haphazard variations, and although it is still a matter debated today, many researchers feel that the variations are due not to the pressures of natural selection but simply to the random ebb and flow of genetic drift.

Recently, a research team led by Gabriel Dover of the University of Cambridge has proposed that a third process might also contribute to evolutionary change, a transforming principle that works not through the external forces of natural selection or genetic drift but through an internal process taking place at the molecular level of the gene itself. Dover and his group call the proposed new mechanism *molecular drive* and note that it should be expected to take place in relatively cohesive populations of a species whose constant sexual interaction has resulted in the entire population possessing roughly the same genetic makeup. In such a population, the genetic makeup of any given creature may be thought of as being crudely analogous to a clock. That is, over long periods of time, the natural changes and permutations taking place within the DNA of any given member of such a population might result in the sudden appearance of a change in form or physiology in the creature. If this was an isolated mutation, in a large population it might not be expected to have much chance of surviving as a genetic characteristic. However, because all members of the population possess basically the same genetic make-up and are, so to speak, running on the same genetic clock, Dover and his group point out that such a change might appear throughout the population simultaneously. Thus, it might have a far greater chance of surviving as a genetic trait in future generations. Dover and his group note that molecular drive would, of course, continue to interact with the ongoing forces of natural selection and genetic drift.

In talking about his hypothesis, Dover says that the notion of molecular drive is compatible with the apparent existence of long periods of evolutionary stability, when a species remains the same for countless generations; the periods may be interspersed with bursts of change, when molecular drive suddenly causes a mutation to spread through an isolated population.[10] Dover's idea is as yet unproven and still highly controversial, but many researchers concede, as Maynard Smith said in summarizing the Cambridge meeting, "Evolutionary biologists are going to have to take molecular biology seriously, especially because of the demonstration of elements in the genome that can multiply outside of the classic Mendelian framework."[11]

The third area of controversy among evolutionary theorists has to do with constraints on the morphologies of new organisms. According to Huxley's Modern Synthesis, species look the way they do as a consequence of utilitarian adaptation to their environments. Such thinking has also always implied that, through adaptation and change, any size and shape of organism are possible. Various researchers at the 1980 conference at Chicago's Field Museum of Natural History observed that not all sizes and shapes of organisms are necessarily possible. For example, most land vertebrates have four legs, not all possible configurations of legs. To the argument that four legs is the optimal design for running on land, it can be pointed out that fish, the ancestors of terrestrial animals, also have four limbs or fins. It can be concluded that four limbs may be the optimal design for locomotion on dry land, but the real reason for this configuration is that the predecessors of land animals possessed the same pattern—evolution is a very conservative affair.

Such conservatism also seems to explain the fact that the embryological process itself is extremely resistant to change. What else might explain why embryos of land vertebrates pass through morphological stages reminiscent of their biological ancestors and develop evanescent gills and associated circulation?

George Oster of Berkeley has suggested that evolution at some level, at least, seems to involve binary decisions. In other words, when a species chooses to take one path in evolutionary development it is, in effect, shutting off other branches of future possibilities. This might explain why an organism might develop scales or feathers, but never a bizarre amalgam of both.[12]

An intriguing twist to genetic theory has been made by zoologist Richard Dawkins of Oxford University, who suggests that genes may be the most ancient self-reproducing entities or *replicators* on the planet—but they are not the only replicators. In his 1976 book *The Selfish Gene,* he asserts that there is a new type of replicator emerging on the Earth. It is still in its infancy, still drifting about clumsily in its primeval soup, but it's already achieved an evolutionary pace that leaves its curious relative, the gene, panting far behind. According to Dawkins's thinking, those replicators are *ideas* and we might call their units of cultural transmission *memes.* States Dawkins's colleague, N. K. Humphrey, "Memes should be regarded as living structures, not just metaphorically but technically. When you plant a fertile meme in my mind, you literally parasitize my brain, turning it into a vehicle for the meme's propagation in just the way that a virus may parasitize the genetic mechanism of a host cell. And this isn't just a way of talking—the meme for, say, 'belief in life after death' is actually realized physically, millions of times over, as a structure in the nervous system of individual men the world over."[13]

Not only are the metaphors we use to invent the universe always changing and transforming, but like biological entities, they are no doubt following their own still-undiscovered laws of evolution, their own survival of the fittest, and perhaps even their own versions of molecular drive and genetic drift.

In this view Darwin's theory of evolution might itself be seen as an organism carrying within it changing memes, much as living organisms carry within them changing collections of genes. Continuing with Dawkins's metaphor, it might be argued that Darwin's theory, remaining viable through so many decades of debates, has proved itself unusually fit as a meme-carrying organism. Like an organism, it has been forced to adapt to a constantly changing intellectual environment. It is still fighting for survival but it is alive and still adapting, and few theorists are willing to predict whether it will look as much like its former self as *Equus* looks like *Eohippus,* or whether it will ultimately become another entity entirely.

# Sociobiology and the Selfish Gene

In the nineteenth century, opponents of Darwin's theories often cited such human traits as cooperation and altruism as evidence that the evolution of human ethical tendencies could not possibly have been the product of natural selection. In the 1930s, the English geneticist J.B.S. Haldane pointed out that an altruistic trait could be favored by natural selection. For instance, if there was one chance in ten that an altruistic act would cost the life of the altruist, but the beneficiaries were the children, siblings, or grandchildren of the altruist—all of whom share more than 10 percent of the altruist's genes—Haldane argued that such a "kin-selecting" altruistic act would indeed bestow an evolutionary advantage on the species. In the years since, numerous other thinkers have expanded upon Haldane's ideas, and the study of the biological basis for various social behaviors is now known as *sociobiology*.

Although it has waxed and waned in popularity since the 1930s, sociobiology has enjoyed a renaissance in recent years. Over the past decade and a half, articles promulgating sociobiological points of view have appeared regularly in the scientific literature, and numerous books have come out on sociobiological subjects. One of the men most responsible for this surge of interest is Harvard professor of zoology Edward O. Wilson. Since the early 1970s, Wilson has published countless books and articles with sociobiological themes, winning a Pulitzer for his 1979 work *On Human Nature*. His detractors have called his ideas trivial and even dangerous. His followers view the newest wave of sociobiological thought as an important new scientific advance and herald Wilson as a worthy successor to Darwin. Wilson himself feels that his formulation of the new sociobiology constitutes "one of the great manageable problems of biology for the next twenty or thirty years"[1] and may even provide humanity's major hope for survival in the future. As he puts it: "We have leaped forward in mental evolution in a way that continues to defy self-analysis. The mental hypertrophy has distorted even the most basic primate social qualities into nearly unrecognizable forms. Individual species of Old World monkeys and apes have notably plastic social organizations; man has extended the trend into a protean ethnicity. Monkeys and apes utilize behavioral scaling to adjust aggressive and sexual interactions; in man the scales have become multidimensional, culturally adjustable, and almost endlessly subtle. Bonding and the practices of reciprocal altruism are rudimentary in other primates; man has expanded them into great networks where individuals consciously alter roles from hour to hour as if changing masks. It is the task of comparative sociobiology to trace these and other human qualities as closely as possible back through time."[2]

Wilson, an entomologist, was first persuaded to adopt a sociobiological point of view about human nature as the result of his studies of insects. In the insect world he repeatedly found the full sweep of social evolution displayed. He also found the omnipresent hand of natural selection. For example, in the leaf-cutter ant *Atta sexdens,* experiments showed that the head width that would have the most energetic efficiency was 2.2 to 2.4 millimeters, and this was precisely the size that Wilson found in their workers.[3] Similarly, the time–energy budgets of a creature's survival needs are scrupulously ingrained in them by nature. Harvester ants devote roughly one-third of their time to work, one-third to rest, and one-third to patrolling their nest, because this breakdown provides them with the optimal survival value. Conversely, mayflies, because they have such a short life span, devote virtually all of their adult lives to reproduction. It would not pay for the mayfly to devote any less time to reproduction, just as it would not pay for the harvester ant to devote any less time to patrolling the nest.

Researchers have long pondered the ability of one generation of a species to pass on a trait to the next. As far back as 1864, evolutionists such as Herbert Spencer were postulating the existence of physiological units, intermediate between cells and simple organic molecules, that were self-replicating and species-specific; but it wasn't until the birth of modern genetics that the gene became an inextricable part of evolutionary theory. The current thinking is that the leaf-cutter ants with head widths of 2.2 to 2.4 millimeters have a greater survival rate than leaf-cutters with other sizes of heads and hence are able to pass on more of their genes to descendants. The gene thus becomes the vehicle of transmission that allows natural selection to work.

In this light, the strategies of existence become the strategies to continue one's genetic inheritance; with this simple realization, Wilson, among others, started deciphering behavior as nature's many elaborate games to preserve and to further genes. Such an interpretation of behavior is obvious in many of nature's strategies. Stags fight each other because such behavior is an advantageous ploy to continue the genetic inheritance of the stronger. A mother tiger defends her young not because nature is inherently loving but because such behavior will continue her genetic line.

Like Haldane before him, Wilson was impressed by the numerous examples of kin-selecting altruism that exist in the animal world, noting that such examples of altruism extend right down to the insect kingdom. For instance, the stinging behavior of a worker honeybee is a very effective defense against attackers, but honeybees who sting do so as kamikaze fighters. In the act of stinging, vital internal organs are torn out of the worker bee's body and she dies soon afterward. Such an act of suicide might seem to be altruism of the highest order, but it becomes much more understandable in light of the fact that worker bees are sterile females.

They have no hope of passing on their own genetic line and can continue their species only by protecting the colony. Wilson describes another example from the insect world: "I have observed that injured workers of the fire ant, *Solenopsis invicta,* leave the nest more readily and are more aggressive on the average than their uninjured sisters. Dying workers of the harvesting ant, *Pogonomyrmex badius,* tend to leave the nest altogether. Both effects may be no more than nonadaptive epiphenomena, but it is also likely that the responses are altruistic. To be specific, injured workers are useless for more functions other than defense, while dying workers pose a sanitary problem."[4]

Wilson found that even the most elaborate insect behaviors could be unraveled in terms of natural selection and the preservation of the gene. His studies of insects culminated in 1971 with the publication of *The Insect Societies,* for he was not content to confine his studies to the world of invertebrates. Time and time again, he concluded that the lessons of insect societies could be extrapolated to the behaviors of more complex organisms; that the same parameters and quantitative theories he had used to analyze termite colonies could be employed to understand troops of rhesus monkeys and beyond.

Wilson conducted an exhaustive study of virtually the entire panorama of vertebrate life, from the dominance systems of birds to the social organization of the Hamadryas baboons, from the scent communication of black-tailed deer to the matriarchal ties of the African elephant. His attempt to meld what he had learned from the insect world with the entire scope of vertebrate life was outlined in his *Sociobiology: The New Synthesis,* published in 1975.

In *Sociobiology* Wilson expanded on his theories about insect behavior and set forth the general biological principles he felt governed the behavior and social organization of the entire animal world. Although, on the surface, survival strategies are as varied as the range of animal life itself, underneath, Wilson still spied the

same basic genetic underpinnings: "Although vertebrates are sel-
dom suicidal in the manner of the social insects, many place themselves in harm's way to defend relatives. The dominant males of
the chacma baboon troops, *Papio ursinus,* position themselves on
exposed locations in order to scan the environment while the other
troop members forage. If predators or rival troops approach, the
dominant males warn the others by barking and may move toward
the intruders in a threatening manner, perhaps accompanied by
other males. As the troop retreats, the dominant males cover the
rear."[5]

Wilson observed that the adults of many species interpose themselves between predators and the young. His explanation, once
again, was that these were examples of kin-selecting altruism.
Dominant males are likely to be the fathers or at least close relatives of the weaker individuals they defend. Thus, by putting
themselves in harm's way, they are helping preserve their own
gene pools.

Even in more complex behaviors, Wilson saw only more elaborate strategies to continue the genetic line. Social organization becomes more and more intricate, but always with the subtle raison
d'être of continuing lineage. Even communication, according to
Wilson, is an intricate survival strategy. The presence of food or
water, the intrusion of a territorial rival, and the appearance of a
predator can all be "read" from the actions of one's neighbors.
Because there is safety in numbers, South American tapirs use a
short "sliding squeal" to stay in touch with each other in the dense
vegetation of their rain-forest habitat. Wilson pointed out that researchers have found that the young of diverse bird and mammal
species utilize distress calls to attract adults to their sides. For example, the vervet *Ceropithecus aethiops,* an arboreal African monkey, uses a lexicon of at least four or five sounds to announce and
to identify enemies. A snake evokes a special *chutter* call, and a
minor bird or mammalian predator elicits an *uh!* or a *nyow!* A

major bird predator, however, evokes a *rraup!* from the vervet. Thus, even rudimentary semblances of language evolve as survival strategies.

Is human behavior driven by the same genetic motivations that are so pervasive in the animal world? Wilson is convinced that a wide variety of human activity and conventions have genetic origins. For example, it might be argued that one thing that sets humanity apart from the animal world is our propensity for producing what we call "art." Wilson cites research from a number of investigators suggesting that artistic impulses are by no means limited to man. In 1962, when Desmond Morris reviewed the subject in *The Biology of Art,* thirty-two individual nonhuman primates had produced drawings and painting in captivity. None of the animals had received special training or, indeed, anything more than access to the necessary equipment. Many of the animals became so engrossed in the activity that they preferred drawing and painting to being fed and, on occasion, even threw temper tantrums when someone tried to take them away from their work. Two chimpanzees in the study were extremely productive. One named Alpha produced over two hundred pictures, while another named Congo, whom Wilson calls "the Picasso of the great apes," was responsible for nearly four hundred. Wilson adds, "Congo's patterns progressed along approximately the same developmental path as those of very young human children, yielding fan-shaped diagrams and even complete circles. Other chimpanzees drew crosses."[6]

Wilson believes that the artistic activity of chimpanzees may well be a special manifestation of their tool-using behavior. As he points out, members of the species display a considerable facility for inventing and using tools. As for why a facility for inventing and using tools might be developed through natural selection, according to a sociobiological point of view, Darwin himself provided an explanation in 1871 in *The Descent of Man:* "If some one

Vervet monkeys show different vocal responses to different predators.

man in a tribe, more sagacious than others, invented a new snare or weapon, or other means of attack or defence, the plainest self-interest, without the assistance of much reasoning power, would prompt the other members to imitate him; and all would thus profit. . . . If the new invention were an important one, the tribe would increase in number, spread and supplant other tribes. In a tribe thus rendered more numerous there would always be a rather better chance of birth of other superior and inventive members. If such men left children to inherit their mental superiority, the chance of the birth of still more ingenious members would be somewhat better, and in a very small tribe, decidedly better."

In a similar manner, Wilson cites other behaviors which might be *filtered out* through natural selection. For example, incest would not be in the gene's best interest due to the fact that bonding between siblings has a greater chance of producing undesirable genetic mutations than bonding among less closely related members of one's group. Wilson points out that studies have shown that a deep sexual inhibition develops between people who live in close domestic contact during the first six years of life, and brother–sister marriage is almost universally avoided in human societies.

Wilson also touches on even more controversial aspects of culture and behavior that he feels are genetically programmed within us. For example, he feels that since xenophobia, the fear of strangers, would have been an adaptive trait for primitive hunter-gatherers, a predisposition to fear outsiders was probably assimilated into man's gene pool. He goes on to suggest that evolution may have even built into us genetic predispositions toward such specialized xenophobias as bigotry and racism. He adds, "It may well be that bigotry and group aggression stem from the interaction of several quite distinct behaviors, including the fear-of-strangers response, the proneness to associate with groups in the early stages of social play, and the intellectual tendency to dichotomize other human beings into in-groups and out-groups."[7]

In an equally delicate area, Wilson suggests that genes also promote behavioral as well as physical differences between the sexes. He cites, for instance, studies of hermaphrodites who are genetic females but acquire aspects of masculine anatomy as fetuses.

Wilson observes that these hormonal and anatomical masculinizations result in a greater frequency of tomboyish behavior and concludes that modest genetic differences predispose females to be less venturesome and aggressive and more intimately sociable than males.

Some critics have accused Wilson of promoting notions of genetic determinism that not only are simplistic but could be used to justify racial and sexual oppression, as in the case of Nazi biologists who provided "scientific" evidence of the superiority of Aryans over Jews and others. Such critics go on to point out that fascists in Great Britain and philosophers of the French New Right have already started quoting Wilson's sociobiological views to support their own extremist beliefs.

Wilson himself considers sociobiology a tool to attack racism rather than a manifesto to support it. Only a greater understanding of the evolutionary roots of racism's blinding emotional power might free humanity from outdated bigotry. Similarly, he does not feel that his theories should lead one to conclude that women should be discriminated against. Instead, he believes that a sociobiological understanding of the differences between the sexes can improve political science by providing more accurate predictions of the costs and benefits of different possible permutations of social institutions.

Wilson's theories have evoked support from growing numbers of scientists and writers who perceive sociobiological explanations in a wide variety of behavioral and cultural phenomena. For example, biologist Randy Thornhill of the University of New Mexico and anthropologist Nancy Wilmsen Thornhill suggest that rape may be genetically programmed into male behavior among both humans and nonhumans. They point out that, as repugnant as it may seem, rape provides a reproductive advantage to the rapist in the form of offspring who would in turn pass on the genetic inheritance of the rapist.

In this regard, rape is not limited to the human world. Scorpion flies, male orangutans, mallard ducks, snow geese, mountain blue-birds, and many species of fish are all known to rape. As Thornhill states, "Rape is the only option for reproduction for a male without resources, because he cannot deceive a female about his quality as a mate."[8]

For example, the courtship ritual of the scorpion fly demands that the male woo a prospective female with a nuptial gift, such as a dead insect or a little ball of saliva. Competition among males is so intense that some males even risk their lives by stealing dead insects from the webs of spiders, their greatest enemy and predator. It is theorized that rape has evolved among scorpion flies for the simple reason that the rapist avoids such risks as the spider's web and consequently his genetic fitness is increased.

In a technological society, however, sociobiologists point out that rape no longer tends to produce offspring. Evolutionary biologists William Shields of the State University of New York and his collaborator Lea Shields point out that rape among humans is most immediately an act of violence, as opposed to a sexual act. Given that rape might be biologically programmed into us, the Shieldses suggest a possible way of ending rape behavior. They cite the fact that human beings are also programmed by natural selection to make learned assessments about risks associated with certain types of behavior. If the cost is greater than the potential benefit, the behavior is unlikely to continue. To eliminate rape behavior, William Shields offers the alternatives of hanging and castration. Both result in genetic death and are therefore the ultimate deterrent. Others have suggested less extreme solutions, arguing that, at least, the punishments culture prescribes for rapists must be enforced if rape is to be controlled.[9]

Sociobiologists have also come up with other controversial conclusions about human nature. For example, from a sociobiological point of view it appears that human beings are much more polygamous than they are monogamous. One study of 853 societies found that having just one mate was the norm in only 16 percent of them. The majority of societies studied, 83.5 percent, were polygynous, allowing men to have more than one wife. A tiny minority, about .5 percent, practiced polyandry, allowing women to have more than one husband.

What determines whether or not a species is polygamous? According to a sociobiological point of view, the decision of a species to opt for either monogamy or polygamy is determined by the amount of time and energy a parent must devote to caring for offspring. For example, among mammals, the female's investment, at least biologically, is considerably larger than the male's. To begin, she contributes an egg that is larger than the sperm (in humans the egg is eighty-five thousand times larger), richer in nutrients, and more precious, since she will produce only a limited number of them throughout her lifetime. Furthermore, she will carry the child and care for and nourish it at least through infancy. This is a huge investment compared to the one tiny sperm among billions that will be contributed by the male. This imbalance, asserts the sociobiologist, is responsible for the fact that polyandry represents such a tiny fraction of the societal norm.

Another factor that comes into play is the male's choice of strategy to produce the most offspring. Is it more advantageous for the male to inseminate as many females as possible, or will more of his progeny have a chance of reaching adulthood if he engenders a limited number of offspring and tends to stay around to father them? In the bird kingdom, staying around and being a good father has proved to be the best strategy. An estimated 91 percent of bird species are monogamous at least during the breeding season. However, sociobiologists point out that monogamy is rare in mammals and appears to be a relatively recent invention of certain human cultures.

One of the most important questions sociobiology poses is, How did life get started in this direction in the first place? In *The Selfish*

*Gene* Dawkins offers a possible answer. According to Dawkins, life began in the primordial soup of the Earth's oceans, and what first set life apart from nonlife was its ability to self-replicate. At first, these early replicators were exposed to the hurly-burly of competition. But, over time, they constructed walls around themselves and were protected in their private little oceans by walls of protein. In the beginning such vehicles were nothing more than enclosing membranes, but slowly the machines became more and more elaborate, until today, 4 billion years later, we have the entire pageant of evolution.

As to the fate of these early replicators, the primordial architects, Dawkins states: "They did not die out, for they are past masters of the survival arts. But do not look for them floating loose in the sea; they gave up that cavalier freedom long ago. Now they swarm in huge colonies, safe inside gigantic lumbering robots, sealed off from the outside world, communicating with it by tortuous indirect routes, manipulating it by remote control. They are in you and me; they created us, body and mind; and their preservation is the ultimate rationale for our existence. They have come a long way, those replicators. Now they go by the names of genes, and we are their survival machines." [10]

From the sociobiological point of view, we are taxis for an amalgam of chemicals. We die, but the gene does not. It never grows old, but leaps from body to body down through the generations, manipulating each individual in turn for its own ends. In this scheme of things, it appears that Samuel Butler's observation, "The hen is only an egg's way of making another egg," has a peculiar truth to it. The gene's predominant goal in "life" is simply to self-replicate. And that, in Dawkin's view, means that the main quality to expect from a successful gene is a sort of "ruthless selfishness." Dawkins makes the point that genes are not conscious of what they are doing. They do not act with any sort of awareness. Only we possess awareness and that, he says, allows us to understand the actions of our selfish genes and at least have a chance to upset their designs. But in his view this does not mean that we can deny that we are still basically products of their selfishness.

Wilson's theories have been strongly challenged by critics. Richard Lewontin, a Harvard zoologist, points out several flaws in the notion that genetic motivations have an all-encompassing control over cultural convention. He observes that gene frequencies change rather slowly in time, whereas cultural changes can occur rapidly. Hence, he feels that a sociobiological approach has little to say about the vast cultural changes that have occurred, for example, between the two-horse carriage and the two-hundred-horsepower Cadillac.

Lewontin also points out that there is hard evidence that genetic differentiation between geographic groups is quite small compared to the variation within groups. Several studies of human gene frequencies agree that 85 percent of genetic variation is between individuals within local populations. He states, "This places the sociobiologist in the absurd position of claiming great cultural importance for very small genetic differences."[11]

Wilson touched upon this problem in *Sociobiology* and postulated the existence of an unspecified *multiplier effect* that would magnify an arbitrarily small genetic difference into an arbitrarily larger cultural deviation. When critics found this vague, he set about to develop his ideas further. In 1981, along with physicist Charles J. Lumsden, he offered a more extensive mathematical model to explain the multiplier effect in *Genes, Mind, and Culture*. In the book, Lumsden and Wilson expanded their thesis: Not only is most of human behavior genetically inspired, but the entire genesis of mind and culture is the ruthlessly selfish gene. According to them, our intense genetic motivations form a feedback loop with cultural convention, causing each to grow and reinforce the other through a process they call *coevolution*. They believe that their mathematical models indicate that evolution and large-scale genetic/cultural changes do not take millennia to occur but can appear in as little as a thousand years.

Lewontin remains skeptical. In a review in the July/August 1981 issue of *The Sciences,* he accused Lumsden and Wilson of tailoring their proof to fit foregone conclusions and argued that they have still not explained the multiplier effect.[12]

Stephen Jay Gould also has problems with Lumsden's and Wilson's views. One of the claims in *Genes, Mind, and Culture* is the discovery of the key to one of the biggest puzzles of evolution, the sudden and rapid increase of the brain from ape to human proportions. They assert that walking upright freed the hands to develop tools, and this in turn caused the positive feedback loop of gene/culture coevolution to lead to an accelerative increase in the brain's size. In other words, using tools made us more clever, which enabled us to develop cleverer tools, which enabled us to become even cleverer, and so on.

Gould has pointed out that this theory is by no means new. As he observes, we have had evidence that upright walking came first and brain development second since australopithecines were first discovered in South Africa in the 1920s. The notion was, in fact, first suggested by Darwin and later expanded on with remarkable perspicacity by Darwin's German champion, Ernst Haeckel.

In Gould's view, Lumsden's and Wilson's theories boil down to the old "nature–nurture" debate, a debate that Gould sees as pointless. In his view, there is really no nature–nurture contradiction as such: "Every scientist, indeed every intelligent person, knows that human social behavior is a complex and indivisible mix of biological and social influences. The issue is not *whether* nature or nurture determines human behavior, for they are truly inextricable, but the degree, intensity, and nature of the constraint exerted by biology upon the possible forms of social organization."[13]

In Gould's mind, simply listing imperatives and specifying the various feedback loops of coevolution is no defense for a naturist bias and no vindication of sociobiology. The issue for him is how shaping and constraining the specified universals are. "The answer," says Gould, "at least from the list [Wilson and Lumsden] provide, is not very much at all. I therefore find this particular invocation of genetics as a newly discovered determinant of social behavior to be both trivial and uncontroversial." [14]

Wilson is undaunted. He still feels that sociobiology will provide us with the information we need to engineer a better society. Although he concedes that the political decisions suggested by sociobiological understandings will be difficult, he believes that the day will come when we form symbiotic relationships with intelligent and decision-making computers who will help us with such problems. Where will this man–machine symbiosis leave us? Wilson replies, "With all our passions and our petty hatreds—plus altruism, propensity toward biophilia, religion, rebellion against authority, sex-bonding and all those other 'contemptible' primate traits that distinguish us from machines." [15]

Whether the sociobiologists are right or wrong in their views, much of their thinking is still based on the notion that the forces of evolution are inherently selfish. But this view has recently been challenged.

# Symbiosis and Cell Evolution

The selfish battle for existence that is the cornerstone of Darwinism has recently been challenged by Boston University biologist Lynn Margulis. Although Margulis accepts that competition is part of the game, she argues that cooperation has played a much more important role than has been hitherto recognized. In her view, complex life evolved because, over half a billion years ago, collectives of bacteria grouped together in cooperative or symbiotic relationships to form more complex organisms.

Margulis's starting point is the fact that the cells of plants and animals have a family of traits in common. All are larger than simple organisms, have meiotic sexual systems—sexual systems in which each parent donates a cell containing a half-set of chromosomes—need oxygen to live, and are composed of cells with nuclei of DNA surrounded by protective membranes. In scientific terms such cells are known as *eukaryotic,* a word derived from two Greek roots that means simply "having a true nucleus." The cells of such organisms as bacteria and cyanobacteria (once known as blue-green algae), on the other hand, are smaller, do not have sexual systems, often do not need oxygen, and do not have nuclei in their cells. Such cells are known as *prokaryotic,* meaning "prenuclear."

Margulis's thesis holds that sometime during the Precambrian period, more than a billion years ago, the Earth was inhabited only by prokaryotes. As these microbes swarmed in the air, on the surfaces of rocks, and in the Earth's seas, they occasionally came together and formed more complex relationships. These relationships probably began when a simple, oxygen-breathing, and DNA-rich bacterium took up residence in an amoeboid organism, such as a microbe known as *Thermoplasma*. At first this residency might have been an invasion, but the DNA-rich bacterium, being more protected from its surroundings by the mass in which it had entrenched itself, might have allowed its host to live. Conversely, the amoeboid organism might also have received something in return. Perhaps the DNA-rich bacterium was able to regulate some function in the mass that had hitherto been beyond its control. Whatever the case, the relationship became symbiotic: Both organisms benefited from the partnership and gained an evolutionary advantage.

Next, Margulis suggests, this partnership might have been invaded by another bacterium, an oxygen-breathing, rod-shaped organism similar to a modern-day bacterium known as *Paracoccus denitrificans*. Again, the rod-shaped bacterium might have had predation on its mind, but on discovering that the cytoplasm of its host shielded it somewhat in its fight for survival, it took up residence. Its host in turn discovered that the rod-shaped bacterium was very good at converting food into energy and regulating the supply of oxygen, and another merger was effected. This, says Margulis, is how the great division between prokaryotes and eukaryotes began. Specifically, she believes that the *mitochondria,* the rod-shaped subcellular components, or "organelles," that regulate the flow of fuel and oxygen in the cells, started at the beginning of evolution as free-swimming bacteria.

To those who think this sounds farfetched, Margulis points out that such mergers still take place among bacteria. In addition, the organelles within our cells, such as the mitochondria, resemble bacteria, possess their own DNA, and contain proteins unlike others elsewhere in cells but like free-living bacteria. And this is not all, perhaps, that we owe to bacteria.

Margulis believes that the nucleated creature that resulted in that first great step from prokaryote to eukaryote also acquired another talent through symbiosis. As that primordial symbiotic complex drifted haphazardly through the water, she believes that it ultimately encountered yet another type of microbial organism, a wriggly, corkscrew-shaped bacterium known as a *spirochete.* The spirochete would have offered a very special talent to the complex. Unlike the complex, the spirochete was capable of locomotion. As Margulis states, "Some of the amoeboids formed associations with spirochetes, which, in search of food, attached themselves to the amoeboids...."[1] In exchange, the spirochete offered the amoeboid the ability to swim under its own power, as opposed to being at the mercy of the ebb and flow of the waters of its environment.

Margulis points out that modern-day spirochetes are still attaching themselves to other microbes and forming similar symbiotic partnerships. For example, in the gut of the Australian termite *Mastotermes darwiniensis* there lives a flagellate protozoan, a smooth-swimming, single-celled organism covered with hairs, or flagella, that propel it oarlike through the water. In standard textbooks the protozoan is known as *Mixotricha paradoxa,* but a closer look at its undulating oars reveals that they are not true appendages but in fact are elongated bacteria that have attached themselves to the surface of the microbe. If one questions the efficiency

---

The common termite of the northeastern United States cannot digest wood without the help of a symbiotic group of microorganisms, known as trychonymphs, which inhabit the termite's intestines. The trychonymph is itself another symbiotic cooperative and each one of the whiplike appendages or flagellates that it uses for locomotion is also a separate organism. Some biologists believe that such symbiotic partnerships may be the means by which the complexities of all life evolved, and as further evidence cite the fact that the mitochondria or subcellular units responsible for oxygen metabolism in the cells of all oxygen-breathing organisms, like the flagellates of the trychonymph, still possess their own unique DNA.

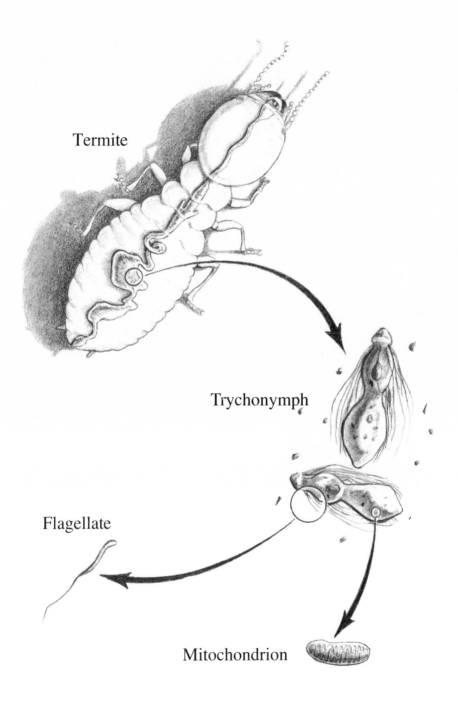

Termite

Trychonymph

Flagellate

Mitochondrion

with which such peculiar collectives work, one need only look at the perfectly coordinated undulations of these hairs, or cilia. Equally striking is the fact that the protozoan lives in the gut of the termite and is a part of a larger symbiotic hierarchy. Without *Mixotricha paradoxa* the Australian termite, and indeed all wood-eating insects, would die, for it is the protozoan and not the termite that possesses the ability to digest the cellulose content of wood. In other words, *Mixotricha paradoxa* is a colony of creatures inhabiting yet another colony of creatures.

It is this colony-within-a-colony aspect of life that Margulis believes has resulted in virtually all animals and plants. And to support her thesis, she has uncovered other clues. For example, the protoplasmic cylinders of some spirochete bacteria contain structurs known as *microtubules*. Such a microtubular structure is also found in the cell whips, or cilia, of all protozoans capable of locomotion, including the sperm tails of plants and animals and even the tails of human sperm. Electron microscopy reveals that this microtubular substructure is everywhere, in the cilia lining our lungs, in oviduct cilia, and even in the cilia that are part and parcel of our sensory organs—the sensitive hairs of our inner ears, the chemical-sensitive hairs in the membranes of our noses, and the light-sensitive rod cells in the retinas of our eyes.

Margulis theorizes that it is through symbiotic processes that much of what we know as the complexity of life has evolved. Not only is human sperm the result of a merger between bacteria, but our senses themselves are products of a skill mastered originally by microbes. The chemistry that allows the cilia of the *Paramecium* to discern when it has been prodded is similar to the chemistry that allows the tiny hairs within our inner ears to discern when we are off balance. As Margulis sees it, the universal presence of the microtubular arrangement of the proteins of virtually all such tubular structures in nature is a Rosetta stone of sorts—once one has learned to decipher its language, one begins to read new meaning into many other biological phenomena. As Margulis states, "The most compelling spinoff of spirochetal proliferation may actually be our brains. Brains and nervous systems are massively composed of the same microtubular structures and proteins which power cilia and cell reproduction. Axons and dendrites, the sensitive extensions of nerve cells guarding the gates of synapses, prevail in the brain. Like the sense organs of the inner ear and the light receptors of the retina they are composed of microtubules. Particularly suggestive is the fact that alpha and beta tubulin are the most abundant soluble proteins in the brain. . . . It is as if the microtubules first used for cell whip and chromosomal movement have been reshaped and usurped for the function of thought. Thinking may be the result of microtubular interaction, of spirochetal secret agents in a new phase of microbial evolution."[2]

In 1967, when Margulis first set down her symbiotic theory of cell evolution and submitted it for publication, it passed over a dozen editors' desks before finally being accepted by the *Journal of Theoretical Biology*. Many members of the scientific community found her notion that human beings are nothing more than co-evolved symbiotic communities of bacteria heretical. However, in the years since, Margulis's ideas have become increasingly respected. As Cyril Ponnamperuma of the University of Maryland states, Margulis's symbiotic theory may become "biology's equivalent to the grand unifying theory."[3]

Perhaps the most interesting thing about Margulis's work is the possibility that cooperation, in addition to competition, has been responsible for some of the major advances in the evolution of life on the Earth. As the late Columbia University philosopher Ernst Nagel pointed out, metaphors arrived at by science often have a powerful effect on the way we view many other aspects of our individual and cultural existence. For example, the Newtonian theory of mechanics and gravitation not only inspired the atomistic analyses of mental phenomena but in times past was used as a premise in arguments for a theistic religion and for a monarchical form of government.[4] Similarly, the preeminence of competition in

Darwin's theories became the rational for laissez-faire economics, for imperialistic foreign policies, for strongly individualistic moral standards, and for various educational programs.

If Margulis is correct in her assertion that cooperation should also be given a starring role in the evolutionary process, there will no doubt be similar implications for such a new view of evolution.

# When Man Stopped
# Being an Ape

In Darwin's day it was shocking even to suggest that human beings were related to chimps and gorillas. Today it has become tolerable among scientists and the intellectually enlightened to believe that we shared a common ancestor with the apes some 20 million years ago. However, there is now persuasive evidence that man and ape split from each other as little as 5 million years ago, and the possibility of this recency has been often ignored by members of the paleontological establishment.

Some of the most outstanding evidence of the closeness between man and ape comes from a battery of techniques developed recently by genetic engineers. Such techniques have enabled scientists to probe deep into the structure of DNA and genes and to actually retrace the evolution of an organism by unraveling the biochemical history of the molecules composing it. Although the preciseness of such techniques is a recent advance, the similarity of the molecules composing man and ape had already been established long before molecular biology had even been conceived. Cambridge biologist George Nuttall was comparing species by means of immune reactions as long ago as 1901.

An American by birth, Nuttall, while doing doctoral research in Germany, came across the revolutionary ideas of Paul Ehrlich, the father of immunology. Ehrlich had discovered that blood contained a substance that would cause certain proteins to precipitate or coagulate. Ehrlich noted, for example, that if small amounts of foreign proteins were injected into an animal, the animal would manufacture what he termed *precipitating antibodies.* After an animal created such antibodies for itself, Ehrlich discovered that it could handle a second injection of the same foreign protein with much more ease. Ehrlich thus concluded that the animal was able to build up an immunity to the invading protein. Ehrlich further conjectured that the antibodies one animal made after injection with the blood proteins of another would react only with blood proteins from animals of the same species as the original donor.

Ehrlich went on to pioneer the use of antibiotic "magic bullets" against disease and won a Nobel Prize in Medicine in 1908. But Nuttall recognized, as he stated in his *Blood Immunity and Blood Relationships,* published in 1904, that "the persistence of the chemical blood relationships between the various groups of animals serves to carry us back into geological times, and I believe . . . that it will lead to valuable results in the study of various problems of evolution." [1]

Not content with just speculation, within a few years Nuttall had conducted over sixteen thousand experiments on over nine hundred specimens of blood taken from a wide range of species. Each experiment consisted of dissolving a small portion of dried blood in a drop of antiserum. There was one kind of antiserum for many species of animal, and Nuttall manufactured his various antiserums by injecting foreign blood proteins into rabbits. He would then allow the blood and antiserum mixture to stand for twenty-four hours, after which he would examine it to see whether there was any evidence of precipitation or coagulation.

Nuttall hoped that his method would develop into a new discipline. Although he was elected a fellow of the Royal Society for his findings, his work fell into obscurity until the late 1950s. At that time, Morris Goodman, a professor of anatomy at Wayne State University School of Medicine in Detroit, began similar studies using a new immunodiffusion technique that had been developed by Swedish scientist Orjan Ouchterlony. It was Goodman who discovered the unexpected closeness between the blood proteins of man and ape.

Since the eighteenth century, when Linneaus formulated the modern system of classifying plants and animals, man has been placed on an evolutionary branch separate from that of the chimpanzee and gorilla of Africa and the orangutan and gibbon of Asia. According to Linneaus's classification, man belonged to the family Hominidae while the apes, both African and Asian, belonged to the Pongidae. However, in his first tests Goodman discovered that the antigens of man and chimpanzee were practically identical. Goodman next tested serum from an orangutan and a gorilla and discovered that man and gorilla appeared to be almost identical. In subsequent tests Goodman was unable to determine whether it was the chimp or the gorilla who was closest serologically to man. It didn't really matter. The upshot was that Goodman had demonstrated that the chimp and gorilla were no closer to each other than either was to man. Hence, Goodman concluded that the chimpanzee and gorilla should not be placed on the same branch of evolution separate and apart from man. According to their blood proteins, the three were equally related.[2]

In the August 27, 1981, issue of *New Scientist,* John Gribbin and Jeremy Cherfas point out that this knowledge should have created a "major upheaval in paleontology," for it effectively redefined the route that man had taken on his path to humanity. Rather than separate from the apes, who then went their own way and divided into all currently known types, it seems that man separated from the chimpanzee and gorilla at the same time that they separated from each other.[3]

While Goodman was redefining his techniques in the early 1960s, an anthropologist named Vincent Sarich was just starting his postgraduate research at Berkeley. Sarich was also a chemist by training, and after becoming familiar with Goodman's work, he realized that there was far more that could be done with protein molecules. One of Sarich's teachers, paleoanthropologist Sherwood

Washburn, learned of his interest and directed him to Allan Wilson, an immunologically trained biochemist also at Berkeley. Using techniques that were similar to Goodman's but of tremendously greater sensitivity and resolving power, Sarich and Wilson devised a way to measure precisely the immunological distance between any two species.

The principle on which Sarich and Wilson based their work is relatively simple. DNA, by the code strung along its length, directs and determines the sequence of amino acids that go into the making of every protein in any given organism. According to current thinking, changes in the DNA, or mutations that lead to evolutionary advance, accumulate with time and are reflected in changes in the protein sequence in the DNA. The immune reaction thus depends on how closely the shape of the subject protein matches the shape of the original antigen. The more similar they are, the stronger their immune reaction and the shorter their immunological distance.

Sarich and Wilson realized that the immunological distance between a subject protein and an antigen also provided a sort of evolutionary timepiece. Every time the strand of DNA protein undergoes a change, it can be viewed as the ticking of an evolutionary clock. Given that proteins accumulate changes at a more or less steady rate, it would be possible, by matching the changes between two related but different organisms, to measure the time elapsed on their evolutionary clocks since they had diverged from a common ancestor. Following this tack, Sarich and Wilson determined that each pair of primate lineages had accumulated the same number of "ticks" since they had split from their shared ancestry. The next task was to calibrate it, to determine how much time was represented by the space between the ticks. To do this they employed a well-established paleontological finding. The fossil record reveals that the amount of time that has passed since the Old World monkeys split from the apes is about 30 million years. Thus, by counting the ticks that had elapsed during that 30 million years and comparing the immunological distance between Old World monkeys and apes, they were able to figure out roughly how much time had elapsed between each tick. According to their findings, man, chimpanzee, and gorilla shared a single common ancestor just 5 million years ago. The evolutionary clock placed the orangutan split at about 8 million years ago, and the gibbon split at 10 million years ago.[4] As Jeremy Cherfas and John Gribbin note, "The paper announcing these results was published in 1967. Paleontologists, sad to relate, have still not absorbed them. To pick a comparably significant development at around the same time but in another branch of science, it is as if theoretical astronomers had ignored the discovery of pulsars."[5]

To help rectify this situation, in 1982 Gribbin and Cherfas, both former editors at *New Scientist,* published their own book, *The Monkey Puzzle: Reshaping the Evolutionary Tree.* They point out that there is other evidence to support the controversial date arrived at by Sarich and Wilson. For example, there is a long-standing mystery about the anatomy of the upper body of men and apes. Both are designed to brachiate, to swing by their arms from branches. The mystery is that there are no fossils of brachiating apes, and those apes whose fossils we do have do not seem to have been brachiators. Gribbin and Cherfas ask, "If apes did not bcome brachiators until after they had split from man some 20 million years ago, then why does man have so many anatomical signs of a brachiating past?" They believe that this suggests that the conservative evolutionary time scale is wrong. Man possesses the anatomy of a brachiator because he split off only 5 million years ago, at a time when the common ancestor of both man and ape was already an accomplished brachiator.[6]

As a result of what paleontologists believe to be ever-more-precise techniques of measuring the immunological distance between organisms, we now know that the genetic makeup of man and chimpanzee is more than 99.5 percent identical. We are more closely related to chimpanzees than horses are to zebras. Nonethe-

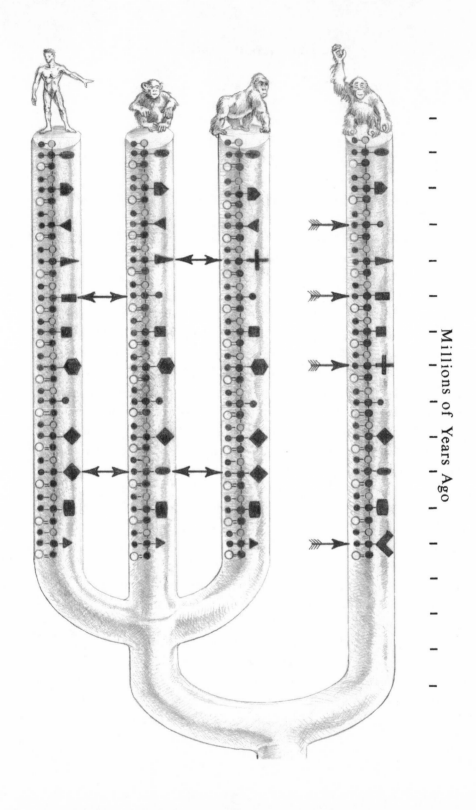

Millions of Years Ago

less, biology books go on classifying man as Hominidae and apes as Pongidae, proposing that man split 20 million years ago, not 5 million. As Gribbin and Cherfas observe, "Most paleontologists, like Leakey, ignore the question, at least in public, assuming—largely wishful thinking—that there is something wrong with the molecular measurements made on living species. This is a classic case of double standards, for those same fossil hunters are generally willing to accept the molecular evidence when it confirms what it does for the horse and zebra, the picture they have sketched out."[7]

As the late biologist René Dubos once stated, "We are human not so much because of our appearance, but because of what we do, the way we do it, and more importantly because of what we elect to do or not to do. Our species acquired its humanness not by losing its animal characteristics, but by engaging in activities and developing patterns of behavior that have led to a progressive transcendence of animality resulting in the creation of humanness."[8]

If the ability of science to reshape our image of ourselves occasionally seems disconcertingly powerful, it should also be remembered that it can be equally fragile. In the next chapter we will explore a recent incident that demonstrates just how fragile it can be.

Man, the chimpanzee, the gorilla, and the orangutan all show a degree of relatedness. One method for determining precisely how related they are is by studying the proteins they have in common (symbolized by the columns in the diagram). If the evolution of the protein molecules composing each has proceeded at a steady rate, then the number of molecular differences in the proteins, shown here by arrows, can be viewed as calibrations in a gigantic evolutionary clock. The less time that has passed between such molecular differences, the greater the degree of relatedness between the compared species.

# Lamarck Lives

In 1980 a respected Australian immunologist named Ted Steele published a book titled *Somatic Selection and Adaptive Evolution,* in which he proposed that certain traits acquired by an organism during the course of its life might be passed on to offspring. This notion was not new; it had first been promulgated by the eighteenth-century French naturalist Jean Baptiste de Lamarck. What was new was Steele's proposal of the mechanism for such a transfer.

Lamarck's original proposition was that characteristics animals acquire during their lifetimes and as a result of their experience might be passed on genetically to their progeny. For example, Lamarck believed that the giraffe's long neck was the result of its constant stretching to reach topmost leaves. Similarly, according to a Lamarckian point of view, if a father was a blacksmith and acquired well-developed muscles in his lifetime, this trait would be passed on to his sons, who would have slightly more developed musculature than they would have had their father been employed in a less strenuous occupation. Half a century later, Charles Darwin disagreed with Lamarck and put forth quite a different view. As Darwin saw it, the giraffe's long neck was the result not of stretching but of the fact that giraffes with longer necks were favored in the process of natural selection. According to Darwin, it did not matter how muscular one's father became during his lifetime; each son would still have to develop his own similar physique through the same hard work as the father.

One of the first individuals to spell out a simple physical explanation for this mechanism was the nineteenth-century German biologist August Weismann. An early supporter of Darwin, Weismann pointed out that the cells of the body, or the *somatic cells,* were obviously modified in response to environmental conditions. If one was a manual laborer, one's hands obviously became callused. However, Weismann proposed that the *germ cells,* the cells in the ova and sperm and the only cells capable of passing on information from generation to generation, were quite independent of the genes within the somatic cells. As Weismann saw it, Lamarckian influences were impossible because there was no mechanism by which somatic cells could feed back information to the genes within the germ cells. Hence, this was the simple physical reason for rejecting Lamarckism.

Weismann formulated his notions at a time when cell physiology was still very primitive and no one had even heard of molecular biology. It wasn't until the 1950s and the work of Francis Crick and James Watson that the situation was put in a new light. Crick and Watson worked out the structure of DNA, the molecular storehouse of knowledge within the cell. In their view—the view that has become axiomatic in modern biology—DNA contains the information to create all of the various substances that the body needs to function. When the DNA wants to create a protein, for example, it does not do so directly. It does so by creating RNA, and it is the RNA that then makes the protein with the aid of a blueprint provided by the DNA.

Many biologists have assumed that these findings support Weismann's original doctrine. Steele disagrees. In his view, Weismann posited that the somatic cells do not and could not feed back information to the germ cells, but Crick's and Watson's doctrine does not assert that the RNA cannot feed back information to the DNA. We now know that there are several mechanisms by which new genetic material can be fed back into the DNA. For example, viruses, which are little portions of nucleic acid cloaked in protective proteins, can enter and alter the original DNA program. This fact was demonstrated in the 1970s by Howard Temin, who consequently won a portion of the 1975 Nobel Prize in Medicine for his protovirus theory of evolution. Viruses are only one of the possible vehicles that can effect such information feedback, a fact that has formed the basis of the new science of genetic engineering. Given that this is the case, Steele considered the possibility that viruses or similar vehicles might carry somatic RNA back into the DNA of the sex cell. Indeed, Temin had already asked the same question in 1971: "In extreme cases one could imagine that a product of protovirus evolution would infect the germ line, become integrated there, and thus affect progeny organisms."[1]

After restating Temin's original proposition in *Somatic Selection and Adaptive Evolution,* Steele and a colleague, Reg Gorczynski, set about to demonstrate such a process experimentally. To do this, they induced a state of immune tolerance in one strain of mice by injecting them with cells from another strain. They then set about to determine whether tolerant fathers could pass on the trait to any of their offspring, a phenomenon that would demonstrate a feedback of information into the germ DNA.

The classic work on tolerance was first performed in the early 1950s by Sir Peter Medawar (for which he received the Nobel Prize), Leslie Brent, and Rupert Billingham. In their original studies, Medawar and colleagues showed that one animal could accept a skin graft from another strain whose cells had been used to make the receiver animal tolerant. This was a difficult and tricky process and required experience to produce reliable results. Steele and Gorczynski therefore decided to employ a different method to determine tolerance, a test-tube experiment that measures the vigor with which an animal's spleen cells attack the cells of the donor strain. This procedure, known as a cytotoxicity test, is also not without its problems, a fact that was to contribute to the controversy that followed.

After Steele and Gorczynski obtained their results, they discovered that somewhere between 50 and 60 percent of the progeny from tolerant fathers seemed to have inherited the trait. As Steele states, "I was stunned. It really worked. They supported the hypothesis." In the second generation of progeny, Steele and Gorczynski found that the frequency of tolerance remained a substantial 20 to 40 percent, although there appeared to be a "waning" effect.[2]

In short, it appeared that animals that had acquired immunological tolerance to a specific test strain were able to pass on the characteristic to the next and subsequent generations at a significant frequency. It seemed that a classic example of Lamarckian inheritance had been demonstrated experimentally. Steele and Gorczynski communicated their results to Howard Temin, who submitted them to the *Proceedings of the National Academy of Sciences* in January 1980. Results of a second series of experiments were submitted to *Nature* on June 11, 1980, and published the following February.

When word of Steele and Gorczynski's findings reached the scientific community, a debate ensued. In spite of the fact that their work contradicted aspects of Medawar's own findings on immune tolerance, Medawar was keen to find out whether Steele's results were valid. A team of researchers led by Dr. Elizabeth Simpson at Medawar's laboratory, working with a team led Dr. L. Brent at St. Mary's Hospital Medical School in London, set about to duplicate Steele and Gorczynski's findings. As Medawar states, "I explained to Steele that the people repeating his work were somewhat prejudiced; they would have *liked* to have found his story to be true, for this would have made us rethink our conventional ideas about the mechanism of evolution."[3]

Many researchers found Steele's conclusions very difficult to accept. As Avrion Mitchison, an immunologist at University College,

London, pointed out, if such apparently Lamarckian processes were a fact, one would be hard pressed to explain the genetic stability observed in most populations.[4]

Such criticisms notwithstanding, what many feel was the final verdict came in when Simpson and Brent published the results of their duplicate experiments in the February 4, 1981, issue of *Nature*. Their data simply did not support Steele's findings. In fact, they obtained results that they felt once again demonstrated that Lamarckian effects did not occur. They attributed Steele's results to faults in his experimental methods. Steele in turn claimed that Simpson and Brent had misread their own findings.

In an assessment of the matter in the March 22, 1981, *New York Times,* Medawar concluded, "When scientists get mutually contradictory results, the important thing is to try to find out why they did so. We cannot put our finger on any single cause of the discrepancy between our results and Steele's, but I feel that in dealing with an intrinsically highly variable system, Steele was the victim—as we all sometimes may be—of a vagary of random sampling that made his results seem much more convincing than they really were. However, the character of science and the apostolic zeal of Lamarckists are such that if Steele's story *is* true, it will in due course be shown to be so. I hope it will be, but fear that—as with all supposed examples of Lamarckian heredity—it will not. The most up-to-date verdict possible is that Lamarck was wrong.[5]

Although the Steele episode did not result in any new scientific breakthroughs, its give-and-take does represent an indispensable part of the scientific enterprise. Determining what is to be considered "real" and what is not is always a very delicate process. Paradigms can be laid to rest almost as quickly as they are created.

It is interesting that any paradigm may rise or fall at any time, but while a paradigm holds, it retains the power to transform our image of ourselves. In the next chapter we will examine what, in the biological universe, may potentially turn out to be the most powerful transformative paradigm of all.

# Genetic Engineering

Molecular biology has been a growing discipline for thirty years, but during the last several years it has experienced an unprecedented level of activity. This is due primarily to the explosion of the new science of genetic engineering. With the advent of the two related technologies of gene cloning and rapid DNA sequencing, science has started to tamper with life itself.

When it comes to studying human beings, the task before the genetic engineer is formidable. Man's forty-six chromosomes contain an estimated hundred thousand genes. So far, only some eight hundred have been pinpointed and mapped, and currently we are only mapping an additional two hundred per year. At the current rate, it will take another five centuries before all forty-six chromosomes have been completely deciphered. However, new technologies will no doubt rapidly speed this process. Dr. Walter Goad, director of the government-sponsored Genetic Sequence Data Bank (GenBank), estimates that it will probably take more than 3 billion characters to encode all of the chemicals in the body in this manner, and the finished "recipe" for a human being will fit on thirty high-density magnetic tapes, taking up less than a four-foot bookshelf.[1]

Still, none of this would have been possible without the development of rapid DNA sequencing. Before researchers could unravel the sequence of the various genes contained in the DNA molecule, they first had to discover a way that such genes could be withdrawn from the nucleus and isolated for study. The first individual to demonstrate that such a process was possible was Stanford biochemist Paul Berg. Berg first employed a DNA-restriction enzyme that cut up the DNA molecule into appropriate and manageable segments. Next, with the aid of a type of virus known as a *bacteriophage,* Berg was able to transfer the isolated gene to another organism, in this case the bacterium *Escherichia coli.* Then, each time the hybrid *Escherichia coli* reproduced, it also reproduced a pure portion of the isolated gene. Not only could the isolated gene then be more easily studied, but because *Escherichia coli* reproduced so quickly, many gallons of such cloned bacteria could rapidly be produced. Later, Walter Gilbert and Frederic Sanger developed a method for determining the sequence of various genes in the DNA molecule, and in 1980 all three men shared the Nobel Prize in Chemistry for their achievement.[2]

With the advent of Berg's, Gilbert's, and Sanger's techniques, new vistas opened up for the molecular biologist. For the first time researchers had a procedure that enabled them to manufacture substances previously obtainable only from natural sources, often with great difficulty and expense. Consider somatostatin, a hormone involved in controlling production of insulin and growth hormone. In 1971, when somatostatin was discovered, it took nearly half a million sheep brains to produce just five milligrams of the substance. Now the same amount can be manufactured in a two-gallon broth of genetically modified bacteria. Similarly, growth hormone, which is used to treat dwarfism, was once obtained only by extracting it from the pituitary glands of cadavers, at astronomical expense. Now, new techniques are enabling companies to consider manufacturing growth hormone at a price affordable for the general public.[3]

These substances are only a few of the hormones and chemicals now slated for genetic manufacture. Others include the enzyme urokinase, used to dissolve blood clots; the hormone thymosin alpha-1, which, it is hoped, can be used to treat brain and lung cancer; beta-endorphin, the brain's own powerful painkiller; interferon, one of the body's own natural defenses against viral disease; and insulin. Interferon is now widely believed to act against certain types of cancer, in particular, cancers of the breast and of the lymphatic system. Before the advent of genetic engineering, interferon had to be painstakingly extracted from human tissue, and a single injection cost around $150. Researchers now believe that all of that is going to change. For example, in December 1980, Sandy Athertone, a Derby, Kansas, housewife, became the first diabetic to be injected with bacterially made insulin. The insulin Athertone used came from the pharmaceutical labs of Eli Lilly, which has spent $40 million to build plants in Indianapolis and outside Liverpool, England, to manufacture insulin genetically on a mass scale.[4] Insulin made by these techniques, although more expensive than insulin from animals, has been on the market for over two years.

Recombinant DNA technology also brings with it the possibility of the manufacture of new vaccines never before possible. For example, in late 1983, scientists of the New York State Health Department announced that through genetic engineering they had developed a vaccine that protected rabbits against hepatitis, and another that protected mice against a type of herpes. It is hoped that a similar set of vaccines may be developed within a matter of years for humans. Some scientists even believe that genetic engineering will enable us to develop vaccines that will prevent cancer. Says Dr. Ivor Royston, a cancer researcher at the University of California, San Diego, "We're on the threshold of developing a whole new form of cancer treatment."[5]

Genetic engineering is already enabling cancer researchers to clone antibodies designed to attack specific cancers. Such current cancer therapies as chemotherapy and radiation treatment tend to attack the whole body in the hope of eliminating cancer cells— what some have called the "shotgun" approach. But such sweeping and destructive shotgun blasts will soon be replaced with infinitely more precise bullets: antibodies designed to attack extremely specific invaders within the body. Says Dr. Royston, "People may look back at conventional chemotherapy and say, 'My God, they used to poison the entire body to kill off malignant cells!'"[6]

New vaccines and pharmaceutical substances are only one of the promises of genetic engineering. While working at General Electric's Schenectady, New York, labs in the early 1970s, microbiologist Ananda M. Chakrabarty discovered that there existed certain bacteria capable of breaking down hydrocarbons. Chakrabarty went on to discover that the genes responsible for this capacity were contained not in the bacterium's single chromosome but in small, auxiliary parcels of genes, known as *plasmids,* in the cytoplasm. Using techniques developed by genetic engineers, Chakrabarty was able to remove the plasmids from a number of bacteria and transplant them into a single bacterium, thereby transforming it into a new crossbreed with a voracious appetite for oil. Freeze-dried until needed and then sprinkled on straw and tossed into the ocean, these super bacteria could presumably make quick work of oil spills. Says Chakrabarty, currently a researcher at the University of Illinois Medical Center, "You can make tons of these microorganisms in a matter of days." Other such superbacteria now on the drawing board include microorganisms designed to manufacture protein for food, to distill alcohol more efficiently, and even to extract metals from low-grade ores.[7]

Because of the commercial applications of genetic technology, it has rapidly become big business for a number of companies and individuals. For example, in January 1976, Robert Swanson and Herbert Boyer each put up $500 to found a company that later became known as Genentech. The purpose of Genentech was to explore the commercial possibilities of gene splicing. On October 14, 1980, the value of each man's holdings stood at slightly more than $82 million. On that day, twenty minutes after the company first put its stock up for sale to the public, the price per share soared from an initial $35 to a whopping $89. When the day closed, the first gene-splicing company to go public had established for itself a market valuation of $529 million, about 8 percent of the value of Du Pont.[8] Not all such ventures have fared so well, however.

Needless to say, the combination of new technology and big bucks brought with it a host of new legal issues. In 1972, when General Electric tried to patent its oil-eating bacterium under Chakrabarty's name, the U.S. patent office balked. They argued that if Thomas Jefferson, who had penned the nation's first patent law in 1793, had intended life to be patentable, he would have said so. And besides, they added, no one had ever tried to patent the Red American Beauty Rose. Nonetheless, when General Electric pressed its case, the Court of Customs and Patent Appeals overturned the patent office's antiquated bias; in June 1980, the U.S. Supreme Court backed them up. As Chief Justice Burger explained, the issue was "not between living and inanimate things, but between products of nature—whether living or not—and human-made inventions." General Electric and Chakrabarty were granted their patent, and currently there are applications for hundreds of different kinds of new, manmade organisms.[9]

Not everyone was pleased with the decision. J. Leslie Glick, president of Genex Corporation in Bethesda, Maryland, argued that it could encourage companies to spend research time on creating modifications in organisms purely for the purpose of making them more patentable. In Glick's opinion, this would be a "waste of research." Stephen Turner, president of Bethesda Research Laboratories, agreed, and said the real beneficiaries of the decision would be patent lawyers. As he quipped, "I call this the Patent Lawyers' Employment Act of 1980."[10]

In the medical arena, genetic engineering is also doing more than just enabling researchers to manufacture new organisms and hence new substances. It is also providing entirely new diagnostic techniques. For example, by using DNA sequencing, a team of researchers at the Baylor College of Medicine in Houston recently uncovered a genetic defect in human chromosomes that increases an individual's susceptibility to emphysema. Prompted by an earlier epidemiological study, the team discovered that people who develop emphysema often have a genetic inability to produce sufficient amounts of a lung-protecting protein. Using a radioactive probe, the team was able to extract some of the substance from a patient's lung cells while it was still attached to the gene that controlled its production. Once this key gene was isolated, it was discovered that people with a genetic propensity for developing emphysema had but a single letter that had been mistyped by nature in their hereditary code. This abnormality, known as a point mutation, has been found to be most prevalent among people with Northern European ancestry. Researchers now estimate that about one out of two thousand people of Northern European ancestry have such a genetic propensity. Arteriosclerosis also has been linked to other such point mutations. Other conditions that researchers suspect might be due to similar genetic misspellings include diabetes, allergies, and even peptic ulcers.[11] The most famous disease known to be caused by a point mutation is sickle-cell anemia.

Again, the new diagnostic techniques that genetic engineering has allowed have created new legal issues. By 1982, according to a survey conducted by the government's Office of Technology Assessment, half a dozen major corporations in the United States were employing genetic testing to spot employees who were likely to have adverse reactions to toxic substances used in the work environment. In addition, another fifty-nine companies have reported that they are considering adopting similar policies. As a result, future job applicants may find themselves turned down because of

---

At the center is a DNA molecule, showing the letters representing part of its genetic code. DNA is stored on chromosomes, shown below although they are not usually visible in most cells. If there is a single error in the DNA—a point mutation—this can produce profound results, as shown in the aberrant red blood cells characteristic of sickle-cell anemia (*above right*).

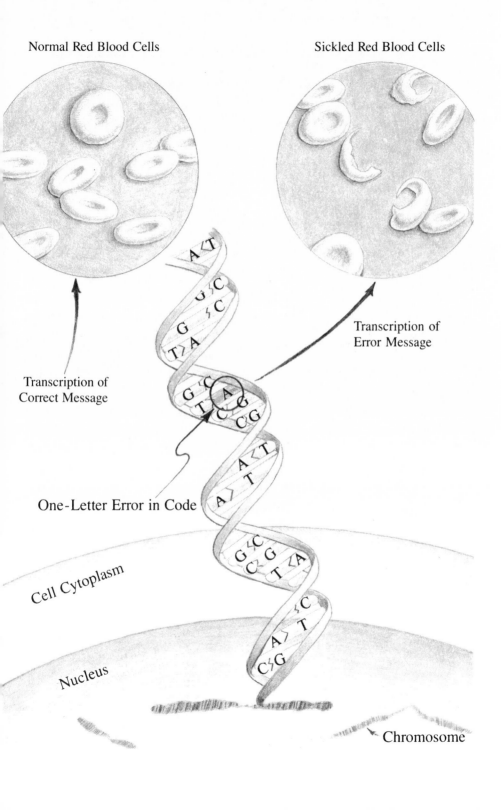

Normal Red Blood Cells

Sickled Red Blood Cells

Transcription of
Error Message

Transcription of
Correct Message

One-Letter Error in Code

Cell Cytoplasm

Nucleus

Chromosome

their genetic background. Critics point out that blue-collar workers aren't the only individuals likely to suffer. Future executives may find themselves passed over for promotion because of possible genetic propensities for heart attacks. In addition, because different genes are distributed unevenly between different sexes and among different ethnic groups, some worry that misuses of genetic data might lead to entirely new kinds of discrimination.[12]

All this aside, for many the most thought-provoking implication of genetic engineering is the inevitability that we will soon be able to redesign the blueprints for organisms far more complex than bacteria. By 1982 researchers were able to transfer certain genetic elements from a rat into the embryo of a mouse and to produce what the media quickly called mighty mice, or mice several times their normal size. Even Paul Berg himself has voiced concern. Immediately after he developed his groundbreaking techniques for toying with the blueprints of life, he penned the now well-known "Berg Letter," which implored fellow researchers to eschew the entire science. Berg was frightened by the implications of his handiwork, in particular by the realization that humanity would soon be able to transform itself. Is it morally right, Berg asked, to actually redesign what we call humanity? Says Dr. Frank Ruddle, professor of biology and human genetics at Yale University, "Morality changes as the times change. What we deem unacceptable today could be embraced by generations in the future."[13]

Whatever side one assumes in the debate, it is clear that genetic engineering potentially offers us our most powerful tool to date to transform ourselves. Whereas most scientific metaphors of the past tended to change our concepts of things human from without, the new gene technology offers us the first valid method of changing our image from within. With the advent of such a powerful transforming tool, the line between concept and reality has blurred even further.

The ability literally to reshape the human form troubles many because of its godlike implications. In the next chapter we will examine what is arguably an even more blasphemous impingement on the realm of the sacred—the elimination of the aging process itself.

# Maximum Life Span

In *The Structure of Scientific Revolution,* philosopher Thomas Kuhn points out that prerevolutionary periods in science are characterized by a proliferation of sound but competing theories about a series of phenomena. In his 1983 book, *Maximum Life Span,* UCLA gerontologist Roy L. Walford asserts that "gerontology, the science of aging, is alive with prerevolutionary fervor as we plunge into the 1980s. Many signs of a major breakthrough are evident." Walford feels that the imminence of such a breakthrough can be gleaned from the gathering momentum of the discoveries now being made in the field.

In Walford's assessment, there are currently six major theories of aging that look promising. He does not pretend to know which will father the breakthrough; perhaps it will be a confluence of several or all.

In general terms, the six major theories can be divided into two groups. The first group can be called *damage theories,* which suggest that aging is a result of the inadequacies in the restorative systems within cells or between organs. For example, one current damage theory proposes that aging is the result of the cumulative and progressive breakdown of the DNA. At one time, scientists thought DNA was very stable and was maintained without change throughout the life of the cell, and even from generation to generation, with only an occasional mutation. It was then learned that a whole host of phenomena are constantly causing damage to the

DNA—from such environmental agents as cigarette smoke, pesticides, radiation, and smog to normal metabolic processes.

Most living organisms have evolved a complex range of repair mechanisms to take care of the constant onslaught of damage. It is important for such damage to be repaired, for DNA is the computer tape that allows a cell or organism to reproduce itself. If such constant sundering of the DNA were not handled quickly, both cells and organisms would reproduce in a haphazard concatenation of forms and qualities that would certainly spell doom for all life. In this regard, there is some evidence that the cell's ability to repair DNA damage diminishes with age. Walford points out that this makes sense, for if repair was perfect, there would be no chance of mutation and hence no process of evolution. It has even been suggested that nature has purposefully set the rate of DNA repair below the rate of damage so that mutations can accumulate and organisms can evolve. In other words, aging is merely a by-product of the repair deficit and a side effect of nature's evolutionary strategy.

This notion was confirmed in a classic experiment performed by Ron Hart and Richard Setlow, who were able to measure the DNA repair rates indirectly in a wide range of animals. They did this by exposing cells from the animals to strong ultraviolet light, which in turn damaged the genetic material within the cells. Next, a collection of enzymes within each cell, the cell's repair system, set about to restore the DNA to its original state. Hart and Setlow were then able to measure the DNA repair level. They discovered that there seemed to be a direct correlation between the rate of repair and the life span of the animals studied. For example, the rate of repair in a longlived man was far greater than the rate of repair in a shortlived mouse.[1]

If aging is simply the result of the repair deficit, Walford points out that it takes no great conceptual leap to imagine that this is a limit that will someday be conquered. For instance, we already know that cancer cells seem to have overcome the effects of accumulating DNA damage and are, for all practical purposes, immortal. Similarly, germ plasma seems to avoid accumulated DNA damage over long periods of time. In this regard, evidence exists that during fertilization, when the winning sperm enters the awaiting egg, an enormous burst of DNA repair activity takes place.[2] Walford suggests that perhaps all we have to do is learn how to induce higher levels of the repair enzymes in our cells to solve the riddle of aging.

Two other damage theories of aging propose that phenomena known as cross-linking and/or free radical reactants are the cause of the aging process. Cross-linking occurs when two molecules or parts of the same molecule bind together. For example, at one time or another everyone has noticed that an old rubber band is weaker and less resilient than a new one. This rubber band is weakened as it ages because the molecules tend to cross-link together. The same process also happens in skin, bone, and other tissues in the body and accounts for why the skin of old people is less soft and more leathery than the skin of a newborn infant. Byproducts of our normal metabolism cause such cross-linking to occur. As Walford notes, this theory has an intuitive appeal, for as most people grow older, they certainly do feel stiffer and less supple.

Free radicals are molecules that possess a free electron and hence an extra electric charge. This extra charge causes them to be voracious, and they will latch onto and chemically combine with a wide range of molecules they might run into. In the process of normal metabolism, our body produces a host of free radicals. Environmental agents such as pollution, radiation, pesticides, and cigarette smoke also produce free radical activity in the body. The problem is that free radicals interfere with the body's normal processes and wreak havoc on the metabolism in general. They can cause skin and tissues to cross-link as well as change DNA. There is evidence that a number of cancers may well be the result of such free radical attacks against the DNA. Again, to counteract free radical damage our bodies have evolved a host of enzymes that defuse these assailants.

The second group of theories of aging that Walford discusses are known as *program theories,* whereby nature has actually programmed the aging process into living creatures. Perhaps there is a portion of our DNA that literally forces our bodies to age. If this is the case, there is again promise that we might soon control the process. As Walford points out, new techniques for genetic manipulation are being developed every day by biochemists and biologists. We now have the technological capability to develop tadpoles from the nuclei of transplanted skin cells from older frogs. This reveals that, at least, the "program" can be switched back to an earlier stage. Similarly, experiments performed by Walford himself along with colleague Sinan Tas have indicated that gene repression associated with aging may involve the formation of bonds between the sulfur atoms in protein molecules tightly associated with DNA.[3] Walford and Tas believe that it is possible to break these bonds and, indeed, Takashi Makinodan of the Veterans Administration Hospital in Los Angeles has succeeded in rejuvenating the immune response in old mice by breaking those exact bonds with a chemical known as 2-mercaptoethanol.[4]

Another program theory proposes that the initiating event of aging might be the release of some destructive agent, such as the massive outpouring of a deleterious hormone. This is what seems to initiate the aging process in Pacific salmon. Hatched in streams from the Columbia River and up the west coast of Canada and Alaska, the salmon spend six months in gravel river bottoms and then a year or so in freshwater lakes. Then they head out to sea. Two to four years later they return, fighting their way back upstream until they reach the exact spot from which they were hatched. There they spawn, and immediately thereafter, their adrenal glands release a massive amount of corticoid hormones into their bloodstream and they rapidly die. Similarly, after the octopus mates, its optic gland releases a hormone overdose that causes the octopus to age quickly and die. Remove the optic gland, and the octopus lives five times its usual life span.

Along the same lines of thinking, one program theory postulates that aging may be due to a slowly developing hormonal imbalance. Some believe that the aging "clock" lurks in the hypothalamus, the pea-size area of the brain that regulates such other activities as hunger, anger, sleep, and sexual desire. Caleb Finch of the University of Southern California has discovered that there is a significant decrease in the level of neurotransmitters the hypothalamus releases as an animal grows older. In turn, a programmed decrease in the level of neurotransmitters released by the hypothalamus results in what Finch has called an *endocrine cascade,* in which the hormone levels in the body are drastically altered in ways that we usually associate with aging.[5]

Another program theory of aging is simply that nature loses interest in an organism once its childbearing years have passed. According to this theory it is not that the body is programmed to age, *per se,* but that the body is not programmed to take proper care of itself once it has served its evolutionary purpose. Without the steady and controlled turn-off and turn-on which regulates childhood, puberty, and other ordered phases of an organism's growth, the organism simply lapses into "uncoordinated" activity and the resulting chaos is what we view as the aging process.

Walford believes that aging may well be the result of two or more of the above-mentioned processes. For example, perhaps there are two aging clocks, one in the brain's hypothalamus orchestrating growth and development, and another in each individual cell. In the early 1960s Leonard Hayflick discovered that individual cells do, indeed, have an inborn limitation to their life span. When separated from an organism and allowed to live *in vitro,* or in a culture dish, and fed with the appropriate nutrients, they will divide only for a set number of times (around fifty). Then they die. Thus, the fifty rounds of division that nature allows most cells is now known as the Hayflick limit. We know, however, that it is feasible that we might someday learn to control and eliminate the Hayflick limit, for, again, cancer cells have learned to transcend this at first seemingly inexorable barrier and can divide forever ad infinitum.

The theory of aging Walford himself favors is the immunological theory, which asserts that aging is the result of a "double dose of doom": one part decline of function and the other part a programmed and active destruction. He feels that gradual deterioration of the immune system, as a result perhaps of DNA damage or free-radical activity, is one important facet of aging. But Walford also feels that it is likely that there is an additional program for aging, probably located in the genes. To substantiate his thesis, he points out that he has been able to demonstrate, along with colleague George Smith, that a small collection of genes located on a single chromosome in vertebrates like mice and men, known as the *major histocompatibility complex* (MHC), has a direct effect on the maximum life span of mice. In their work, Walford and Smith have developed strains of mice that are genetically identical except for differences in their MHC, and they have discovered that variations in this single chromosome result in significant life span differences among the strains. Walford states, "Our demonstration of these differences provided the first direct evidence that MHC is an important regulator of the rate of aging."[6] Researcher Ed Yunis of Harvard has also confirmed Walford and Smith's findings.[7]

Walford adds, "It must be more than chance that a number of other genes regulating aging besides those directly controlling immunity are also associated with the MHC and reside on the same chromosome. These include superoxide dismutase certainly, and possibly catalase, two of the body's own, intrinsic (self-produced) free radical scavengers. It includes also the level of the second messenger substance involved in the response to many hormones. And Dr. Kathleen Hall and I have found that the level of DNA-repair may be influenced by the MHC."[8]

As an indication of what is to come, Walford says, "Information is already available to enable one to live to be more than 120 years old if he begins early enough and adheres religiously to a lifelong regime of dietary restriction." The basis for this assertion is the discovery by Clive McKay of Cornell during the 1930s that underfed rats had extended their life spans by as much as 50 percent. McKay's results have since been reproduced many times, and Walford himself, along with colleague Richard Weindruch, has also duplicated the experiment. Walford stresses, however, that such underfeeding involves *undernutrition*—a restricted-calorie diet, but with a balanced nutritional content—and not malnutrition. It is now known that undernutrition extends the life span of many creatures. For example, when the carnivorous microorganism *Tokophyra* is allowed to feed freely, it can survive for ten days at most. But when it is allowed to feed only twice a day, it can then survive for as many as eighty days.

Not everyone has greeted Walford's book positively. In their November 1983 issue, the editors of the *Harvard Medical School Health Letter* criticize his view that the connection between undernutrition and life span in laboratory animals necessarily implies anything about a similar effect in humans. They argue that the food used in the rat experiments was designed to make the animals grow and reproduce rapidly, and to this end it is very high in protein—which may shorten the animal's actual life span. As they state, "To draw the conclusion that people will live longer if they keep themselves semi-starved requires two assumptions: 1) that the current human diet is equivalent to the rat's laboratory chow, and 2) that people respond to this diet in the same way as rats. It is already known, however, that the second assumption is false. To take just one example, the potential for bone growth areas is kept open much longer than in fed animals."[9]

Walford counters by pointing out that the *Letter's* assertion that food used in such studies is designed by veterinarians to promote rapid growth is "unacceptably uninformed, being itself nearly a decade behind the published literature on the subject."[10]

Walford foresees that the imminent major extension of the human life span will totally change the structure of life as we know it. He states, "Scientists engaged in research which may have a large impact on society are often blamed for not thinking in advance about the possible effects of their work."[11] Walford firmly warns that the time has come to start thinking about the sociopolitical effects of greatly extended life spans.

Yet for some, the conquering of the aging process seems far less attainable and of less immediate importance than the conquering of many of the numerous causes of death.

# The Oncogene

Cancer is not one disease, but a generic term that applies to more than a hundred different pathological conditions. Cancers of the breast, of the colon, and of other organs come in a variety of forms, each varying in its ability to spread, the ease with which it may be spotted by the body's immune system, and its responsiveness to different treatments. In addition, the typical cancer cell possesses over a hundred traits that set it apart from a normal cell. One of the most obvious of these is its uncontrolled growth rate. Others include its abnormal shape, its failure to respect territorial rules that confine normal cells to particular tissues, its ability to import sugar molecules at an unusually high rate, and its unusual reliance on anaerobic metabolism—a primitive energy-converting process that does not depend on oxygen, as normal cell processes do.

One question that has plagued cancer research is whether each of these traits was acquired individually and as a consequence of a discrete step toward the initiation of a cancer or *carcinogenesis*. In other words, does the normal cell pass through a hundred different stages before it transforms into a cancer cell, or does the complex transformation occur all at once? Even twenty years ago the evidence suggested the transformation occurred all at once. Marguerite Vogt and Renato Dulbecco, then at Caltech, were able to transform normal cells into cancer cells simply by applying a DNA virus known as the polyoma virus to hamster-embryo cells growing in laboratory dishes. When young rats were inoculated with the altered cells, they quickly developed tumors. Vogt and Dulbecco had demonstrated that normal cells could be induced to undergo transformation in a petri dish. No longer was carcinogenesis a mysterious process taking place only within an animal's inaccessible tissues.[1]

Since the virus that induced the transformation was a DNA virus and worked by manipulating the genetic material within the cell, it was suggested that the induced cancer therefore had some sort of genetic basis. Twenty years ago, this was still a highly speculative idea. It wasn't until other evidence started coming in that the notion of a genetic basis for cancer started to gain increasing attention. For example, it was discovered that many nonviral carcinogens, including various forms of radiation and a wide range of chemical agents, also induce genetic changes within the cell.

The problem of obtaining such direct evidence was formidable. The demonstration required the analysis of the complex DNA within the cell itself, not the relatively simple DNA of a tumor virus. The human cell contains as many as a hundred thousand genes spread along the thin, chainlike DNA molecule. The tightly coiled and threadlike DNA within a single human cell stretched out straight would have a length of six feet. In fact, if all of the DNA in a single human body were laid end to end, it would stretch from here to the Sun and back again four hundred times.[2]

It was not until the advent of recombinant DNA technology that the prospect of learning more about this library of information came within our grasp. With the discovery of such tools as various enzymes that could select portions of the genetic material, researchers were able to begin probing deeper into the DNA coil itself. Enter Robert Weinberg. Six years ago, Chiaho Shih, working at Weinberg's molecular biology laboratory at MIT, set out to perform what would prove to be a landmark experiment. Shih's goal was to find the answer to a very important question: Could the transforming cancer trait from a malignant mammalian cell be transferred to a healthy mammalian cell by the transfer of the

DNA molecule? To answer that question, Shih employed a technique that had been developed by researchers in the Netherlands a few years before. The method involved trapping DNA molecules in crystals of calcium phosphate, enabling them to be removed from one cell and implanted in another.

Shih extracted DNA from the cancerous tumor of a living mouse and transferred it to healthy mouse cells in a culture dish. The cells of the healthy mouse were designated NIH3T3. Two weeks after the donor DNA was applied, transformed cells began to appear in NIH3T3. When the transformed cells were injected into healthy mice, the mice developed tumors. As Weinberg pointed out in the November 1983 issue of *Scientific American,* the lesson was clear: The information for being a tumor cell had been transferred from one cell to another by the DNA molecule. It was concluded that whatever was causing the cancer could at least in part be traced directly to information encoded in the DNA.[3]

Shih's experiment was informative, but the most basic property of the tumor-DNA's transforming principle had yet to be established. Was it assignable to a particular segment on the DNA, or was it assignable to several independent genetic elements acting in cooperation to bring on carcinogenesis? Further experimentation began to suggest that it was assignable to a localized portion of the DNA segment. For example, it was found that if DNA was taken from healthy cells that had been transformed into cancerous cells and inoculated into a second set of healthy cells, a few transformed cells appeared a second time. When the experiment was repeated a third and even a fourth time, a scattering of transformed cells continued to appear. Since successive extractions and related manipulations had a tendency to break up long strands of DNA into thousands of small segments, only a few of which could be expected to enter any single mouse cell, it was strongly suggested that the transforming principle occupied a relatively small portion of the DNA strand.[4]

The next problem was to isolate the transforming segment and to study it. The design of such an experiment was dictated by the DNA structure. The DNA molecule is a double helix composed of two strands of paired, three-part molecules known as nucleotides. The totality of genes within the cell or *genome* is composed of some 6 billion base pairs of nucleotides. An average gene comprises five thousand to ten thousand of such pairs. The challenge for Weinberg was to locate the single genetic segment containing the transforming principle among a millionfold excess of unrelated genetic material in the cell.

Weinberg used a newly developed technique of gene cloning, a process that enables retrieval and reproduction of a single genetic segment from the cellular genome, resulting in a large quantity of the pure gene. Weinberg chose the aforementioned method of gene cloning involving the *bacteriophage* virus. To repeat: In the process the cellular genome is broken into several hundred thousand segments. Each of these segments is then inserted into the genome of a bacteriophage. The tampered bacteriophage in turn is allowed to infect the bacterium *Escherichia coli,* where it proceeds, with the help of the *Escherichia coli*'s internal biology, to make many copies of itself. When this takes place in a culture dish, the progeny of an individual bacteriophage quickly kill off the host bacterium and go on to infect any adjacent bacteria. Within a few hours an individual bacteriophage can create thousands of clones of itself, each containing a reproduced portion of the hitchhiking DNA that was inserted into it at the outset. A collection of thousands of different hybrid bacteriophages is often called a genomic library, because in the aggregate they carry the entire store of genetic information that was in the original cellular genome. Weinberg thus had at his disposal a method of dividing up the genome of a cancer cell into hundreds of thousands of packets. The problem became figuring out which of the packets contained the transforming segment. Weinberg named this mutating factor the *oncogene.*

To find the oncogene, he employed a variation on the old parlor

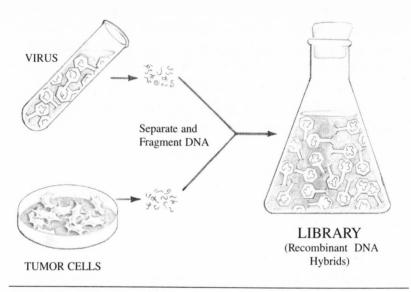

VIRUS

Separate and
Fragment DNA

TUMOR CELLS

LIBRARY
(Recombinant DNA
Hybrids)

To isolate a single point mutation from among thousands in a cancer cell containing an oncogene, a DNA molecule from the cancer cell is broken up and combined with DNA fragments from virus cells. In turn, these are mixed with enzymes to form recombinant-DNA hybrids that possess traits from both their cancer-cell and virus progenitors.

game of Twenty Questions. First, a genomic library was constructed containing the DNA from a chicken lymphoma cell. The resulting collection of several hundred thousand hybrid bacteriophages was then divided into ten sublibraries. DNA was next extracted from bacteriophages in each of the ten sublibraries and injected into healthy cells in culture dishes. Whenever DNA from one of the sublibraries resulted in a carcinogenic transformation, that sublibrary was further divided into ten more sublibraries, each of which was again tested to see if it contained the transforming principle. In this way, the original library of hundreds of thousands of segments of DNA was exponentially narrowed, until the search routine eventually led to a single bacteriophage clone capable of transforming activity. When that happened, Weinberg knew that he had isolated an oncogene.[5]

In the instance of the oncogene responsible for human bladder carcinoma, Weinberg discovered that the difference between a normal strand of DNA and one that would produce a cancer, like the one bolt that may weaken the entire bridge, was but a single variation in one chemical subunit among six thousand. That minuscule change, Weinberg believes, is responsible for directing the cell to manufacture a flawed protein that ultimately develops into a malignancy. As Weinberg states, "Once the oncogene gets going, it wreaks havoc in the cell and the end result is cancer."[6]

To date, three other types of human tumors have been traced to their respective oncogenes. Many researchers caution, however, that Weinberg's discoveries do not mean that we have solved all of the mysteries of cancer, but many in the field are heralding the discovery of the oncogene as the most important advance in cancer research in years.

The discovery of the oncogene in just these few cases of cancer also enables us to entertain questions never before possible. For example, Weinberg asks, "Why are genes maintained in the human genome that, with slight alteration, become agents able to transform cells and generate tumors? Why should an organism carry the seeds of its own destruction?"[7] Although the full answer to this question awaits further research, we can solve part of the puzzle. The particular segment of DNA that is susceptible to the minute alteration that can cause it to become an oncogene is called a *proto-oncogene,* and as Weinberg points out, proto-oncogenes would not have been conserved in the genome if they did not have some vital role in normal cellular function. Weinberg has also discovered that relatives of human proto-oncogenes have been found in the DNA of a number of mammals, in chickens, and even in the fruit fly *Drosophila.* These findings indicate that the ancestors of

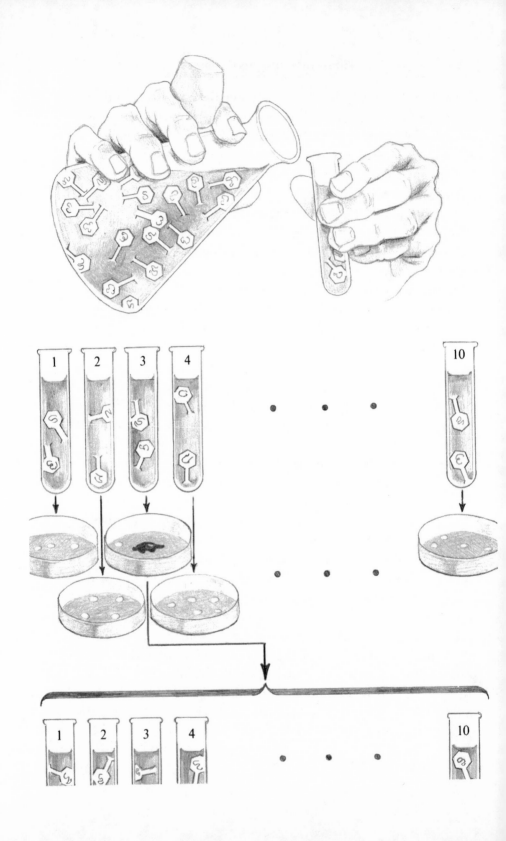

human proto-oncogenes must already have evolved when a common ancestor of human beings and flies lived. Proto-oncogenes would not have been preserved in the genome for such a long time unless they were and continue to be indispensable to the cell, although the precise role of such genes in normal metabolism remains to be discovered.[8]

Weinberg's discovery has opened the door to new technological approaches in the study of cancer. As Jonathan Logan and John Cairns of Harvard appraised his discovery in the November 1982 *Nature*: "Above all, we need to keep in mind that natural human carcinogenesis is a multistep process. We do not know what the rate-limiting steps are, nor which of them are most sensitive to environmental influences and therefore a proper object of preventative strategies. But we can at least feel that the technology for studying genes and their patterns of expression are now advancing so fast that the molecular biologist will soon be telling the epidemiologist what to look for."[9]

To determine which of the thousands of resulting DNA fragments contains the oncogene, the entire "library" of viruses is divided into ten groups, which are then tested. As in a game of Twenty Questions, the positive test group is in turn divided into ten smaller groups, which are again tested, and so on, until the DNA segment containing the single point mutation or oncogene is found.

# What Is Life?

It seems obvious what is alive and what is not. Human beings, ostriches, and sequoia trees all look and act very differently from rocks, sand, and other nonliving things on the Earth. Even though it is easy to describe differences in behavior and structure between a paramecium and a pebble, it is surprisingly difficult to capture the differences between the two in precise definition. For many years now, scientists have been groping for just such a precise definition, and recently a number of researchers have offered some new insights.

A definition that has been offered in the past is that a living thing is a group of cells containing nucleic acids and proteins. Several examples indicate problems with this definition. A recently killed animal contains cells, nucleic acids and proteins, but it is obviously not alive. Hence, it seems logical that an accurate definition of life should include some reference to behavior. But even if behavior is included in the definition, there are problems. For example, there is a very small insectlike animal known as the tardigrade. A spoonful of tardigrades can be completely dried out and stored in a bottle on a shelf for many years. For all intents, they seem dead, but as soon as water is added they will come alive

---

Some scientists believe that, just as a living cell regulates its own internal chemistry, the fact that the Earth regulates its own ecological balance indicates that it, too, should be considered a unit of life.

again. Were the tardigrades alive while they were completely dried out and dormant? And if we consider that they were, how can we define the difference between inactive but alive tardigrades and an inactive but dead dog?

Delving into the world of the very small, we run into other perplexities. Viruses clearly have some of the properties of living systems but lack significant others. They seem alive in the sense that they are capable of movement and are composed of protein shells containing nucleic acids. Unlike most living things, however, they lack the ability to reproduce themselves without depending on more evolved forms of life. They are like chemical computer cards able to penetrate a host, such as a bacterium, and program the bacterium to create more viruses. But they cannot create more of themselves by themselves. It is thus difficult to view them as separate organisms. They seem to be complex chemical systems intermediate between life and nonlife.

At the other end of the spectrum, an even more novel concept of what is alive has been offered by physicist James Lovelock. In his 1979 book, *Gaia: A New Look at Life on Earth,* Lovelock points out that the Earth's atmosphere and oceans possess some extremely unusual traits that one would not expect to have evolved as a result of purely random processes. The temperatures, alkalinities, and chemical compositions of the atmosphere and the oceans are extremely constant. Unlike other planets in the solar system, the Earth's atmosphere contains a high concentration of oxygen that remains constant in spite of the presence of nitrogen, methane, hydrogen, and other potential reactants in the atmosphere. As Lovelock observes, such planetwide anomalies have existed for millions of years, and he attributes their remarkable age and constancy to one thing—the presence of life on the Earth. As Lovelock sees it, the Earth's atmosphere and oceans are maintained as a highly sophisticated buffering device by the totality of life on the planet. Life creates for itself a *biosphere* in which to live, and in this sense the entire Earth functions as a single self-regulating organism.[1] In the words of William Blake,

> Each herb and each tree,
> mountain, hill, earth and sea,
> cloud, meteor and star,
> are men seen afar.

Lovelock calls the organism *Gaia,* after the Greek goddess of the Earth. Lovelock's view that the Earth is itself a living organism challenges dictionary definitions of what is alive.

Columbia physicist Gerald Feinberg and New York University chemist Robert Shapiro offer yet another definition of life in their 1980 book, *Life Beyond Earth: The Intelligent Earthling's Guide to Life in the Universe.* According to Feinberg and Shapiro, the most useful definition of life involves two quintessential points. First, any useful concept of life must be part of a larger and more inclusive concept of a biosphere.

Is an ant colony or a city a living thing? From a human perspective, the individuals that constitute such entities seem to be the most plausible units of life, but as Feinberg and Shapiro note, perspectives can be very misleading. To an intelligent bacterium, a human being would be seen as just a loose association of independent cells. Because divisions between organisms are often indistinct, Feinberg and Shapiro conclude that individual organisms are thus unsatisfactory units of life. They argue that many previous definitions of life have failed because they have neglected to distinguish this crucial relationship between part and whole. In trying to define the term *life,* it seems more and more, as naturalist Loren Eiseley put it, that "a name is a prison—language creates an invisible prison. Language implies boundaries. A word spoken creates a dog, a rabbit, a man. It fixes their nature before our eyes; henceforth their shapes are, in a sense, our own creation. They are no longer part of the unnamed shifting architecture of the universe. They have been transformed as if by sorcery—into a concept—word—boundaries upon the cosmos."[2]

As Feinberg and Shapiro see it, because the various hierarchies of organisms in the Earth's biosphere are so complexly interlocked, it is the biosphere itself that makes the most logical unit of life: "Some striking concepts emerge when we accept the idea that the biosphere is the fundamental unit of Earthlife. The history of Earthlife then becomes the tale of the continuous survival and evolution of the biosphere from its origin on the prebiotic Earth. Replication and subdivision into organisms and species have been strategies adopted by our own biosphere to ensure its own survival, but they need not be the methods used by an extraterrestrial biosphere. A biosphere that has not specialized into many quasi-independent living things is easy to imagine and presumably existed at an early stage in the evolution of the Earth."[3]

But what features of the biosphere identify it as alive and distinguish it from a nonbiosphere? Given that the same general kinds of physical and chemical processes take place among the atoms of living things as in nonliving things, Feinberg and Shapiro propose that it is futile to search for unique structural and functional distinctions at those levels. A more plausible candidate for the feature that distinguishes life from nonlife is the organization or orderliness of the atoms in living things compared with those of the nonliving. The question, What is life? therefore becomes, What is order?

According to Feinberg and Shapiro, order exists when a narrow selection has occurred among equally probable choices. The more improbable or nonrandom an organization of matter and energy, the more probable that it is ordered. For example, there are millions of possible organic molecules that could have arisen naturally on the Earth. We find vast concentrations of a few thousand of them, however, and very few or none at all of the remaining millions. These improbable concentrations are evidence of the sort of order that distinguishes a biosphere from a nonbiosphere. Similarly, we may view a crystal as possessing order, but when we compare it to the complexity and the improbably narrow selections inherent in a biosphere, the differences are profound. In Feinberg and Shapiro's view, there is more order in a biosphere, and it is a much more likely candidate for what we should categorize as life.[4]

Feinberg and Shapiro have pondered the possible shapes and forms that life may have assumed in biospheres other than the Earth's. The evolution of individual living things may be only one strategy a biosphere might take. There may be biospheres in which individual living things did not develop, in which entire planets may be covered with a single, gigantic organism. Feinberg and Shapiro do not believe that self-replication is an essential part of life. Replication is a strategy for increasing order, but it also has its disadvantages. In a biosphere that chooses replication as a strategy, replicated forms must compete with their myriad copies for the energy and materials they need to maintain order. Feinberg and Shapiro thus envision biospheres in which replication either did not arise or has slowly ceased to be a strategy.

They consider the possibility of life based on ammonia, on silicate, or even on petroleum. They contemplate living balloons filled with hydrogen in the upper atmosphere of Jupiter and superoxide-eating lichens on Mars. Perhaps their most interesting contribution lies in their consideration of the possible life forms in biospheres alien to that of the Earth's. They entertain the idea of life as radiant energy living in the "radiobiospheres" of interstellar clouds and feeding on X-rays and ultraviolet light. They even contemplate the existence of plasma life, organized patterns of magnetic force, living in the upper surfaces of stars. Liberated by their own definition, they contemplate the existence of ordered biospheres in the most unexpected areas of the universe.

The most significant point made by Feinberg and Shapiro is not in the myriad of life forms they ponder but in the implications of their conclusions. That is, that life is not an isolable "something" as easily defined as a carbon atom or as a volt of electricity. It is a quality that depends on the degree of order or information in a system. What we define as alive has less to do with process, biochemical or otherwise, and more to do with concept. Thus, to the question posed by this chapter, one might answer with the words of Wallace Stevens:

> Life consists
> of propositions about life.[5]

# Part IV

---

# THE MATHEMATICAL UNIVERSE

**E**instein once remarked that "mathematics is a wonderful gift which we neither understand nor deserve." In this section we will see that not only do mathematicians continue to invent entirely new and abstract worlds but mathematics, in concert with computer science and the expanding new field of artificial intelligence, is in the process of inventing the most interesting new technology of all—machines capable of mimicking the human thinking process.

Norbert Wiener once warned that the computer revolution should be greeted as being even more transformative than the Industrial Revolution was. As Wiener pointed out, whereas the Industrial Revolution changed society, the computer revolution will change the nature of change itself. For just as the Industrial Revolution extended our muscle power, computers are extending the powers of our minds, the organs responsible for inventing the technology in the first place. With the advent of computers capable of mimicking human thought, the inventing process will bend back in upon itself; what new universes this feedback loop between man and machine will invent is anyone's guess.

As Wiener cautioned, the only thing that we can be assured of is that this "new industrial revolution is a two-edged sword. It may be used for the benefit of humanity, but only if humanity survives long enough to enter a period in which such a benefit is possible. It may be used to destroy humanity, and if it is not used intelligently it can go very far in that direction."[1]

The choice is ours, for the new Frankenstein monster is awakening.

# *Fractals*

Imagine that you are in an airplane one mile up, and you take a photograph of an island's coastline. You have decided to trace the island's coastline but in a way that would be easy to describe mathematically. To do this, you have chosen to employ nothing but very short straight lines. With a ruler and pen, you draw on the photograph short straight line after short straight line until you have completely traced around the island's shape. The result is a crude geometrical description of the island.

Clearly, it is not the most accurate geometrical description of the island. You could construct a more accurate outline of the island by taking another photograph from half a mile up and following the same method. But again, it will not be a precise description, only a crude approximation. You could continue the process, taking photographs at lower and lower altitudes (or photographs of greater resolution) until you had drawn around all of the island's bays, headlands, cliffs, boulders, rocks, pebbles, grains of sand, and so on, ad infinitum, but in the end the geometrical shape that you will have arrived at will be so unwieldy that it will itself be just another irregular shape, little better than no mathematical description at all. On account of the infinite irregularity of many shapes of nature, infinite geometric descriptions would seem necessary to define them precisely.

In 1977 Benoit B. Mandelbrot, a noted mathematician and former professor at the University of Paris, published a work titled

*Fractals: Form, Chance, and Dimension,* in which he proposed a simple and elegant way to quantify the irregular shapes of nature. The coastline of an island, for example, is not constructed according to regular Euclidean dimensions. It is neither straight, nor circular, nor elliptic, but meanders in a way that has previously defied precise mathematical description. Drawing on the work of others, Mandelbrot devised a geometry that described such irregularities precisely by employing a group of mathematical entities he called *fractals.* Fractals are important in that they provide physicists and engineers with a method for quantifying things never before quantifiable. In their simplest sense, fractals are not whole numbers or shapes but are mathematical relationships with an ability to describe infinitely complex irregular shapes.

Mandelbrot discovered that although the number of different levels of order, such as the line tracings on the island photographs taken at different altitudes, may be infinite, the relationships between successive hierarchies or successive sets of line tracings made on the photographs is extremely regular—so much so that they can be predicted by employing what Mandelbrot called a *fractal curve,* a mathematical entity that has a very regular and precise numerical value. This value represents the ratio of change between one hierarchy or one set of lines on the island photographs and the next. The ratio is sometimes equal (either exactly or on average) to a whole number; sometimes to a fraction. For example, the fractal describing the ratio at which the fractal curve of the coastline of an island curves in is 1.2.[1]

Because Mandelbrot's fractals can predict the relationship between one hierarchy and the next ad infinitum, fractals provide a way of precisely defining the infinite, but without resorting to an infinite description. An analogous situation might be the description of the value of *pi* (the ratio of the circumference of a circle to its diameter) by a similarly simple and concise formula, without resorting to the impossible task of computing *pi* to an infinite number of decimal places.[2]

In addition to providing mathematicians with a valuable tool for describing the infinite irregularities of nature, Mandelbrot has also shown that the fractal dimensions of a wide variety of natural phenomena are surprisingly similar. For example, the fractal curve of a meandering river also has a dimension equal to about 2. Landscape surfaces are about 2.2. Lung branches, about 2.9. The movement of turbulent fluids, 2.55. Blood vessels, 3. Cloud surfaces, 1.3. And hierarchies of clusters and superclusters of galaxies, about 1.23. Mandelbrot's fractals have also provided a means of systematizing a host of mathematical entities, and they have given physicists a more precise way to describe a variety of natural phenomena, such as Brownian movement—the random, zigzag motions of particles in a liquid or a gas—or the hierarchy of density fluctuations in a fluid at the critical point where it cannot be properly considered either a liquid or a gas. Thus, fractals are more than just a mathematical entertainment, providing a useful tool for both physicists and engineers.

The fact that the coastline of an island and the meandering of the human circulatory system bear a remarkable mathematical relationship to each other suggests that nature perhaps employs still other undiscovered mathematical laws in its designs. Recently a branch of mathematical study has been resurrected to explore this general issue.

# Catastrophe Theory

In the early twentieth century, the British biologist D'Arcy Thompson noted that the forms of many living things resembled the structures of certain nonliving phenomena. For example, the form of a jellyfish bears an unusual resemblance to the shape of a drop of ink diffused in water. In his classic *On Growth and Form,* Thompson wrote, "The waves of the sea, the little ripples on the shore, the sweeping curve of the sandy bay between the headlands, the outline of the hills, the shape of the clouds, all these are so many riddles of form, so many problems of morphology."[1] Thompson wondered whether there existed some abstract and purely geometric theory of the morphogenesis of living organisms that might predict their shapes and dimensions independent of the biological forces that created them. Such morphogenetic constraints certainly seemed to govern the drop of ink. For example, after falling a few centimeters, a drop of ink hits the surface of a glass of water and, stopped by the liquid, gives birth to a vortex ring. Then the vortex ring disintegrates into three or four droplets, each of which, falling, gives birth to small rings. Each time the experiment is performed, each individual vortex ring will be slightly different, but still such differences seem to be oscillations about a mean; certain mathematical laws still seem to hold the diffusing droplet to the same basic geometrical shape. Speculating on whether similar laws might apply to living things, Thompson stopped short of supplying a mathematical formulation for his notion.[2]

Recently, René Thom, a prominent French mathematician, has suggested that catastrophe theory, a branch of mathematics that deals with certain modes of discontinuous change called *catastrophes,* might be able to supply biology with just such a construct. In his book *Structural Stability and Morphogenesis,* first published in French in 1972, Thom wrote that the parameters governing the curve of a swallow's tail can be represented by an intriguingly concise mathematical equation. Moreover, Thom observed that the curve defined by the equation is echoed throughout nature in a variety of phenomena, both living and nonliving. Thom proposes that virtually all forms in nature can be represented by mathematical models he calls *morphogenetic fields.* He further postulates that the final physical form of such natural phenomena can be represented by an *attractor* within that morphogenetic field and that all morphogenesis "can be described by the disappearance of the attractors representing the initial forms, and their replacement by capture by the attractors representing the final forms."[3] In other words, if one imagines the droplet of ink as it falls through space, the mathematical model or attractor, governing its form, first draws it into the shape of a sphere. Then, when it hits the water, another attractor draws it toward the shape of a vortex ring. Then another causes the ring to disintegrate into three or four droplets, and so on. Thus, morphogenesis can be seen as a series of attractors pulling an object into a progression of forms or morphogenetic fields.

Thom's notion of a morphogenetic field is somewhat similar to the notion of morphogenetic fields described by the British biochemist and plant physiologist Rupert Sheldrake in *A New Science of Life.* The difference is that Sheldrake's morphogenetic fields are fields in the same sense as *fields* spoken of in physics. Thom's morphogenetic fields are mathematical representations and do not depend on any particular scheme of causal explanation. As Thom states, his models imply nothing about "the ultimate nature of reality."[4]

Thom believes that formulating a succession of mathematical models might be a better way of trying to understand such unsolved riddles of science as the embryonic morphogenesis of multicellular organisms. Such an approach is unique in that it might be able to predict the evolution of an organism's structure without making any reference to the organism's genetic makeup. As Gerald Feinberg observes, this is roughly analogous to trying to decipher through mathematics what a computer might be capable of doing, without making any reference to the actual hardware of the computer.[5]

Catastrophe theory might even have more sweeping applications than just to the understanding of biological structure and embryonic development. It may be able to define certain parameters of behavior as well. As Thom states, "It is striking to observe how efficiently the capture of prey is realized even at the lowest level of the phylogenic tree. This forces us to postulate that each animal has an organic chart of its mobility that enables it to control its own actual movements with remarkable precision so as to capture its prey or flee from its predators."[6] Thom suggests that such behavior might be governed by genetic forms of motor action that, again, can be represented by mathematical parameters. He believes, in fact, that someday catastrophe theory might even supply mathematical models for such wide-ranging phenomena as dreams, play, the invention of tools, and even the development of language.

Thom's theories have been greeted with mixed reactions by the scientific community. Sheldrake criticizes Thom on the grounds that he does not address the issue of reality or make an attempt to explain the phenomena he is describing in terms of causality. As Sheldrake states, "The problem with this approach is that it is essentially descriptive; it does little to *explain* morphogenesis."[7]

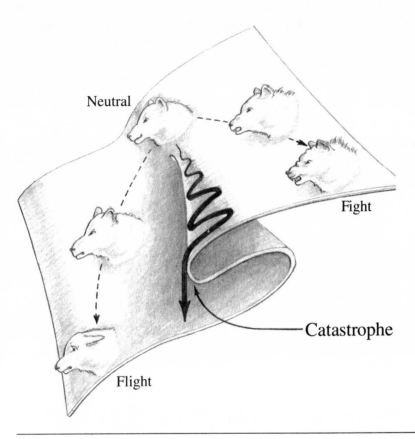

An example of catastrophe theory. The behavior of the husky is plotted on a folded graph. When the behavior of an ambivalent dog is near the crease in the graph, the behavior can suddenly jump from apparent neutrality to either the flight or the fight response, illustrated by catastrophe theorists as a jump in the crease area of the graph.

Feinberg expresses a different sentiment. He says, "It is too early to tell how successful [Thom's] program will be. It has already produced much more extreme polemics than is usual in mathematics. However, I am convinced that whatever the fate of catastrophe theory in particular, the general notion that Thom has expressed, which is that some of the behavior of objects is a consequence of universal mathematical relations, is likely to survive, and provide important insights for future scientists."[8]

Feinberg's prediction has already partly come true, for in the next chapter we will find that scientists have recently found mathematical relationships lurking in what was once thought to be the most impenetrable of all nature's phenomena—in the depths of what was previously defined as *chaos.*

# Chaos and Strange Attractors

The word *chaos* in everyday parlance refers to a state of utter confusion. In nature, examples of chaos include everything from the turbulent flow of water at the base of a waterfall to heart fibrillation that marks the onset of a heart attack. Until recently scientists believed that such phenomena were controlled by laws that were so complicated and unpredictable that they had best be left alone. But now dramatic strides have been made in formulating a mathematical understanding of chaos, and many scientists believe that such advances may ultimately suggest ways of predicting weather and earthquakes, of explaining economic trends, of unraveling the mysteries of epileptic seizures, and may even spawn a new revolution in physics.

Much of the responsibility for the new science—so new that it does not yet have a name, just a nickname, *chaos*—can be attributed to a thirty-nine-year-old Cornell physicist named Mitchell Feigenbaum. Feigenbaum's first key breakthrough came in 1976 and 1977, when he discovered regularities in the behavior of certain simple mathematical equations when they were operated upon themselves over and over again. When manipulated in this fashion, the equations would at first produce an orderly and logical series of numbers, and then suddenly begin producing a disorderly and chaotic string of numbers. The significance of Feigenbaum's discovery was that he also discerned that the transition from order to chaos in these simple equations occurred in a patterned way, a way involving a phenomenon known as *period doubling.*

To visualize what is meant by period doubling, imagine a population of antelope. On a limitless African veldt, such a population might grow smoothly from year to year, and biologists could describe its growth mathematically using a somewhat simple linear equation. However, in a more realistic situation, say, on an African veldt of finite size, such a population would continue to grow only until it had expended its available food supply. Then it would dwindle until the grasses on the veldt had a chance to replenish themselves. Then it would grow again, waxing and waning with the passing of each growing season. Although the equation would no longer be linear, the oscillation of such a population of antelope could still be described by a relatively simple equation.

As the years continue to pass, the waxing and waning of such a population might undergo several possible changes. One possibility is that, like a pendulum swinging, the oscillations would gradually slow down until the number of antelope became stable from year to year. However, if the population were more extreme in its oscillations, or, in the words of Princeton biologist Robert M. May, if the population was more "boom-and-busty," after a certain amount of time it might settle down not to one stable number but to two different numbers in alternating growing seasons.[1] After this, if the population was boom-and-busty enough, the period of oscillation might change to two years and then four, and so on, until suddenly it disintegrated into chaos, and the population level in any given year was completely unpredictable. Such a pattern of increasing bifurcations is what is known as period doubling.

What Feigenbaum discerned in his simple equations was not only that they underwent period doubling during their transition from order to chaos but also that the period doubling occurred at precisely the same mathematical pace, a ratio of transition that was *always* 4.669201 . . . At first Feigenbaum assumed that the number had something to do with the particular equations he was examining. But to his great surprise, he discovered that completely different equations also exhibited the same ratio when they passed from order into chaos. Feigenbaum had discovered a new universal.

Feigenbaum tried to publish his findings in numerous academic journals, but all of them rejected his papers. It wasn't until 1978 that a research team in France discovered Feigenbaum's universal while performing experiments involving the dynamics of fluids. Recognition followed quickly.

Feigenbaum says that it did not matter that his papers were rejected for publication by the academic establishment. As he points out, the dissemination of important information is no longer restricted to what is printed in the journals. In the current era of photocopying, a great deal of exchange goes on through the mail, and because of this, Feigenbaum's ideas were becoming known to a small coterie of kindred thinkers.

One of those kindred thinkers was May himself. As early as 1976, May published an article in *Nature* urging his colleagues to start paying attention to the strange behavior that cropped up when simple equations were made to act upon themselves. As a result, a number of biologists were beginning to think that they were glimpsing something of importance even before Feigenbaum made his historic breakthrough.

Feigenbaum had found a way to study the borderline between order and chaos, and it is now believed that period doubling and the 4.669201 . . . universal underlie many natural phenomena, from the transition of liquids and gases as they become turbulent to the aforementioned fibrillations of the human heart as it passes into the chaos of a heart attack. Even epileptic seizures may involve an element of period doubling. During an epileptic seizure, a few neurons in the brain begin to fire erratically and somehow are able to blow into an uncontrolled electrical storm that temporarily overtakes the entire brain. How the activity of a localized area of the brain is able to effect a breakdown in the entire neural network is still a puzzle, but it is believed that the mathematical techniques now being evolved to study chaos will lead to new insights.

Period doubling may also underlie certain phenomena that are entirely products of the technological age. For example, Paul E. Rapp of the Medical College of Pennsylvania points out that as the interconnections that are being installed between computer networks grow more complex, such systems are becoming "more biological." As such, Rapp fears that complex electronic networks are becoming increasingly susceptible to forms of failure previously observed only in biological systems. Given the growing understanding of how a few maverick elements in an ordered system can suddenly push the entire system into chaos, Rapp fears that computer networks of sufficient complexity are becoming increasingly vulnerable to modes of failure analogous to biological convulsions—their own special form of epilepsy. As evidence Rapp cites a 1979 military experiment designed to simulate the communications traffic that would result from a conventional war. Much to the military's surprise, at a certain level of communications traffic, the entire system simply lost coherence and collapsed into chaos. Officials later reported that at times during the exercise they wondered if they were playing the same game. Other reports of possible "computer epilepsy" have also surfaced, most recently in one that involved the accidental firing of a computer-activated missile from an airplane.[2]

The growing understanding of the rules controlling period doubling is only one of the tools currently enabling researchers to begin to unravel the secrets of chaos. Another is a class of mathematical devices known as *strange attractors,* a term coined by David Ruelle of the Institute of Advanced Scientific Studies at Buressur-Yvette, near Paris, and Floris Takens of the Mathematics Institute of the State University of Groningen, the Netherlands. In some chaotic systems, when one begins to represent the variables of the system as dots on a computer screen, a special kind of design can appear. When a line is drawn through the various dots, it is found that it curves in on itself again and again, almost as if it is attracted to the geometric shape that it assumes. Another odd trait possessed by these geometric shapes or strange attractors is that when they are magnified, each of their parts is found to be a smaller representation of the whole; and on even greater levels of magnification the design repeats again—infinitely it seems—like an endless sequence of Russian dolls one inside the other or the eddies within eddies in a pool of turbulent water. The discovery and study of strange attractors have allowed scientists to find hitherto unexpected similarities in different chaotic systems, further indications of hidden order.

Another key feature of strange attractors is their extreme sensitivity to initial conditions, a property first identified in 1963 by Edward Lorenz of MIT. Lorenz's field of specialty was long-range weather forecasting, and what he discovered in particular was that a very small input could quickly develop into a tremendous difference in output. This idea is now informally referred to as the *butterfly effect*, referring to the idea that the flapping of a butterfly wing in New York today may set into motion a sequence of events that will result in a hurricane in the Caribbean next month. Similarly, and translated into terms of strange attractors, it is found that the trajectories of attractors that begin at almost the same point may still diverge drastically as they develop.

Unfortunately, Lorenz's work was published mainly in meteorological journals, and few physicists appreciated his findings. Even as recently as five years ago, when the butterfly effect turned up in equations, it was often assumed to be a numerical error. It has only been in the past several years, with the advent of new ways of understanding chaos, that it has become recognized as a legitimate phenomenon.

Although the butterfly effect may continue to keep long-range weather forecasting from ever becoming a 100-percent certainty, many researchers are confident that the study of chaos will at least allow them to make inroads never before felt possible. Chaos research has already shed some light on one long-standing extraterrestrial meteorological anomaly. For centuries scientists have wondered about a natural phenomenon known as Jupiter's *Great Red Spot*. It is known that the Great Red Spot is a stationary vortex amid the icy blasts and storms of the Jovian atmosphere, but what is not known is how the Great Red Spot manages to be so stable.

Recently, Harvard astronomer Philip S. Marcus, armed with new understandings about chaos, fed a numerical simulation of the Jovian atmosphere into a Cray computer and had it calculate and plot out how various sets of initial flow patterns would change over time within a particular zone. Marcus found that, regardless of the atmosphere's initial state, after a sufficiently long time, an oasis of order often formed on such a rotating and turbulent surface. He discovered that if a spot formed, it would happen rapidly, within a single Jovian year, and yet the spot would last a long time. He found also that, like Jupiter's Great Red Spot, such an oasis of order would form near the equator as opposed to near the poles; and that if more than one spot happened to form, they would rapidly drift and coalesce into one large spot. As he stated, "What I've done is a numerical simulation that shows that if one looks at a wide range of initial conditions, one gets either no spot or just one spot. That's an empirical, numerically observed fact."[3]

Fortunately such longlived vortexlike features do not form in the Earth's atmosphere because the Earth's surface is broken up by continents. But Marcus speculates that the large vortexlike features that are observed within ocean currents, such as the Gulf Stream, may be analogous to Jupiter's Great Red Spot, and hence subject to as-yet-undiscovered laws governing chaos.

Perhaps the most exciting potential use of the new science of chaos is its application in quantum physics. Currently, this application is the subject of heated debate, but at least some theorists believe that a new type of chaos, called *quantum chaos,* does indeed exist. This belief has been bolstered by a recent experiment.

The experiment was performed by Peter Koch, a physicist at the State University of New York at Stony Brook, and physicist David Mariani of Schlumberger-Dahl, with the findings interpreted by Roderick Jensen of Yale. In their experiment, Koch and Mariani shot a beam of hydrogen atoms through a microwave cavity in which they could vary the electric field. They then measured the number of ionized atoms that emerged and found that in a low-intensity field the beam was not ionized, but in a high-intensity field the entire beam emerged ionized.

States Jensen, "Quantum mechanics tells you that ionization comes from the absorption of photons at precise frequencies. But in the experiment, the frequency of the beam didn't correspond to any photon absorption frequency. There is no quantum mechanical explanation for it."[4]

In assessing the results of the Koch and Mariani experiment, Joseph Ford, a physicist at the Georgia Institute of Technology, concludes that perhaps there are types of chaos in subatomic phenomena that are not accounted for by quantum theory. Says Ford, "If so, the theory is incomplete and we may have to go back to the beginning."[5]

Ford goes on to suggest that results such as those produced by the Koch and Mariani experiment indicate that the study of chaos is emerging as a third revolution in physics, following on the heels of relativity and quantum theory, and there are many who think that this is a possibility. Even if this does not prove to be the case, most at least concede that the study of chaos is closing the gulf between the knowledge of what one thing—one water molecule or one neuron—does and what millions of them can do.

# Cellular Automata

In the 1950s the mathematician John von Neumann was working on devising a machine capable of reproducing itself. Von Neumann was not interested in actually building such a self-replicating robot but was more concerned with whether such a thing was logically and technologically possible.

The solution to his problem ultimately came from an entirely unrelated area. At the same time von Neumann was also supervising the design of the computers being used in the Manhattan Project. It was in this capacity that he encountered a computer game devised by mathematician Stanislaw M. Ulam. Ulam had discovered that when programmed with certain relatively simple formulas, a computer would print out a constantly changing pattern.

The best way to visualize Ulam's game is to imagine the graphic display sometimes put on by the placard-holding sections of audiences at football games. Each member of the section holds a different-colored placard, and there is a well-coordinated plan for which ones to hold up at which time. Imagine, however, that instead having an elaborate succession of placards to display, each audience member has only two, a black and a white one, and is told to follow a simple rule—say, to hold up the same-color placard as a majority of his or her four nearest neighbors—front, back, left, and right—held up during the previous move. The result would be not a preplanned sequence of pictures but a constantly changing series of abstract patterns.

This is basically how Ulam's game worked, only instead of a football audience, the computer is programmed to create an imaginary two-dimensional universe composed of a checkerboard of square cells (or sometimes triangular or hexagonal cells) and instead of placards the computer is programmed to color in each cell or to leave it blank, according to a predetermined rule similar to the football crowd's. What von Neumann found is that when such a sequence of patterns is set into motion, certain organizations or groups of cells seem to take on a life of their own and begin to reproduce themselves, almost as if they were little automata. He concluded that if such self-reproduction was possible in an imaginary but logically consistent world, there was no logical contradiction in the concept of a self-reproducing machine in the real world.

Von Neumann's investigations of such cellular automata remained a mathematical curiosity until 1970, when mathematician John Horton Conway of Gonville and Caius College of Cambridge University resurrected it in the form of a mathematical game called Life. Introduced to the world of computer enthusiasts by Martin Gardner in his *Scientific American* column, Life quickly captured the imagination of thousands. What fascinated computer enthusiasts about the game was that, by programming a simple rule into such a cellular grid system, an entire world could be evoked, a landscape populated by its own objects and phenomena—shimmering forms called *Gliders* that coalesced and floated across the computer screen; others known as *Eaters,* cellular patterns capable of devouring smaller nearby cellular patterns; others known as *Oscillators,* cellular patterns that moved back and forth between one pattern and another; and numerous others.

The surge of interest in such cellular automata has ultimately led researchers to recognize their potential use as models of some physical systems. One physical system in which cellular automata seems particularly useful is the modeling of snowflakes. How do molecules of water "know" how to arrange themselves to form the elaborate symmetries of a snowflake? There is no architect directing the construction, and no individual water molecule carries within it a picture of the entire snowflake it will form. The pattern of a snowflake arises entirely from the short-range interaction of many identical units. Each molecule of water responds only to the influence of its nearest neighbors, but somehow a consistent structure is arrived at, containing perhaps as many as $10^{20}$ water molecules.

One way of understanding how this occurs is to imagine that each site where a water molecule might situate itself is governed by a rudimentary computer. As the snowflake crystal grows, each computer surveys the sites immediately surrounding it, and like a cellular automaton, determines by the fixed rules of its own computational program whether its own site should be occupied or left empty. As the snowflake crystal expands further, ensembles of water molecules continue to function as rudimentary computers— or cellular automata—making the same decisions over and over again in larger and larger hierarchies of ensembles.

One researcher who has recently done a great deal of work on cellular automata is physicist Stephen Wolfram of the Institute for Advanced Study in Princeton. Wolfram, whose work has focused on one-dimensional cellular automata, as opposed to two, has found that they can be divided up into four distinct classes. One of these, a class of automata Wolfram labels Class 3, possesses characteristics strikingly similar to those of strange attractors. This class of cellular automata may further our understanding of such phenomena as the weather, ocean waves, and even the flow of blood through the circulatory system.

Of the four, however, Class 4 automata are the most intriguing and may function as "universal computers." The concept of a universal computer was first put forward by the British mathematician Alan Turing, who is also famous for having deciphered the German "Enigma" code during World War II. What Turing demonstrated was that it was theoretically possible to construct a relatively simple computer capable of performing any possible calculation. Such a theoretical mechanism is now known as a universal Turing machine.

Wolfram believes that his one-dimensional Class 4 cellular automata, given the proper encoding, are capable of simulating "any other system."[1] Cellular automata, according to Wolfram, may help us arrive at a completely new set of rules for how the real world works and, because of their similarity to self-organizing phenomena in the biological world, may even help us to unravel some of the hitherto inscrutable mysteries of living systems such as how life arose out of inanimate elements in the first place.

Another group that has recently investigated other practical applications of cellular automata is the Information Mechanics Group of the Laboratory for Computer Science at MIT, consisting of Edward Fredkin, Norman Margolus, Tomasso Toffoli, and Gerard Y. Vishniac. For example, Vishniac and others in the MIT group point out that physicists usually must rely on differential equations to model various physical systems, but cellular automata provide a fundamentally new way to model processes in the physical world. In this regard, Vishniac points out that two phenomena that are readily modeled by cellular automata are percolation and nucleation, processes of importance in solid-state physics.[2]

Another advantage of cellular automata is that they can be simulated on even the smallest computer. Some researchers point out that many simulations in physics involving cellular automata can be done more effectively and more cheaply with a small computer than with more powerful computer facilities.

Fredkin has even suggested that information, not mass or energy, may be the ultimate stuff of the universe, and that the universe itself functions like a giant computer. This universal computer itself is composed of hierarchies of cellular automata. In other words, in Fredkin's universe, an electron is little more than a pattern of information in motion and possesses no more substance than a changing pattern passing through the placard-holding section of a football audience.[3]

Last but not least, researchers such as W. Daniel Hillis of MIT's Artificial-Intelligence Laboratory believe that the concept of cellular automata may also help in the design of a new breed of supercomputers currently under construction in both the United States and Japan. One of the problems inherent in the construction of this new breed of supercomputers is precisely how to connect vast numbers of individual processors in unison to gain the greatest computing capability. Because it seems that nature may reduce the complexities of its own computing operations into interlocking hierarchies of cellular automata, Hillis believes that a similar advantage might be gained by designing supercomputers along the same lines.[4]

# The Fifth Generation
# of Computers

No issue has loomed more provocative in the history of the development of the computer than the creation of a machine capable of thought. Such a Frankensteinian concept encroaches on territories more often considered sacred than technological, and not surprisingly, our mythologies are filled with instances of such creations, from Pygmalion's Galatea to the talking mechanical head of Friar Bacon. In *Beyond Modern Sculpture,* art historian Jack Burnham spends over four hundred pages arguing that in some strange and Faustian way the desire to create artificial intelligence has been the deep-rooted impetus behind the entire history of sculpture.

The artificial-intelligence (AI) issue challenges our notion of self. It challenges our understanding of intelligence, of logic, of technology. It challenges our economy, and there are some who assert that it even challenges the future balance of world power.

Some doubt that artificial intelligence is even possible. In his 1979 book *What Computers Can't Do,* philosopher Hubert L. Dreyfus of the University of California at Berkeley argues that computers will never be capable of thinking. He feels that it simply isn't possible to break down intelligence into a series of isolable rules and then program them into a machine. According to Dreyfus, "A person experiences the objects of the world as already interrelated and full of meaning. There is no justification for the assumption that we first experience isolated facts or snapshots of facts or momentary views of snapshots of isolated facts and *then* give them significance."[1]

Computer scientist Roger Schank of Yale University perceives other problems: "The thing is, AI is very hard," he observes. Even approaching its creation raises hard questions: "What is the nature of knowledge? How do you abstract from existing knowledge to more general rules? How do you modify the knowledge when you fail? Are there principles of problem-solving that are independent of domain? How do goals and plans relate to understanding?"[2]

Despite the technical and conceptual difficulties outlined by such theorists as Dreyfus and Schank, there is a growing camp of theoreticians who feel that the development of artificial intelligence is just a matter of time. Stanford computer expert John McCarthy, one of the founders of the AI field and inventor of the term *artificial intelligence,* states, "The alternative is to say that there is an area of nature that is not reachable by science. And nothing in the history of science supports that hypothesis."

Nonetheless, the problem remains that even among the believers there is no consensus on how to approach AI. McCarthy believes that the solution lies in programming computers to reason according to well-worked-out languages of mathematical logic. Another founder of the AI field, Marvin Minsky of MIT, believes that the computers should imitate the way the human mind works, which he feels is almost certainly not with mathematical logic. In logic, Minsky is convinced that "the idea of 'fact' and the idea of 'truth' are no good. I think facts and truth are only good in mathematics and that's an artificial system. Logical systems work very well in mathematics, but that is a well-defined world. The only time when you can say something like, 'If a and b are integers, then a plus b always equals b plus a' is in mathematics."[3]

He goes on, "Consider a fact like, 'Birds can fly.' If you think that common-sense reasoning is like logical reasoning then you believe that there are general principles that state, 'If Joe is a bird and birds can fly then Joe can fly.' But we all know that there are exceptions. Suppose Joe is an ostrich or a penguin? Well, we can axiomatize and say if Joe is a bird and Joe is not an ostrich or a penguin, then Joe can fly. But suppose Joe is dead? Or suppose Joe has his feet set in concrete? The problem with logic is that once you deduce something you can't get rid of it. What I'm getting at is that there is a problem with exceptions. It is very hard to find things that are always true."[4]

Gregory Bateson pointed out a similar problem with logic—that it is a poor model for cause and effect. We are blinded to this fact because, as it happens, we use the same words when we talk about logical sequences and about cause and effect. For example, we say, *if* Euclid's postulates are accepted, *then* two triangles with three sides of one equal to three sides of the other are equal. We also say, *if* the temperature falls below 0 degrees C, *then* water starts to turn to ice.

The phrasing of each of these situations causes our "thinking" minds no difficulty, but if they were programmed into a computer, major problems might result. The reason for this, as Bateson pointed out, is that the *if . . . then* of causality contains *time,* but the *if . . . then* of logic is timeless. Because of this difference, the mapping of cause-and-effect sequences—especially when they are circular or more complex than circular—onto the timeless sequences of logic could result in paradoxes that pure logic could not tolerate.

For example, a simple buzzer circuit could be constructed in which the following causal sequences are operable:

*If contact is made at A, then the magnet is activated.*

*If the magnet is activated, then contact at A is broken.*

*If contact at A is broken, then the magnet is inactivated.*

*If the magnet is inactivated, then contact is made at A, and so on.*

However, if the *if . . . then* junctures of this causal sequence were mapped over the *if . . . then* junctures of a logical sequence, havoc would result:

*If the contact is made, then the contact is broken.*

*If P, then not P.*

As Bateson summarized: "Thirty years ago, we used to ask: Can a computer simulate *all* the processes of logic? The answer was yes, but the question was surely wrong. We should have asked: Can logic simulate all sequences of cause and effect? And the answer would have been no." [5]

Proponents on both sides of the logic/antilogic debate offer further solutions to the problems that each approach encounters. Ironically, their solutions are surprisingly similar. Minsky proposes an approach he calls *frame systems*. In the "birds can fly" problem, he would program the computer to analyze the situation in different *frames*. For example, if the frame of the situation happened to be a forest, he would program the computer to consider *flying* a more probable attribute. If the frame of the situation happened to be Antarctica, because penguins live in Antarctica he would program the computer to consider *flying* more improbable. [6]

Employing a methodology he calls *circumscription,* McCarthy would program a list of predicates called *prevented from flying* into the computer. Such a list would include penguins and ostriches, as well as dead birds, or birds with their feet in concrete. In this approach the computer would reason, "If Joe is a bird and Joe is not a member of the set 'prevented from flying' then Joe can fly." [7]

On the surface such discourse may begin to seem simplistic, but if an artificially intelligent machine is developed, there is a possibility that it may be very much like a child; that it will have to be taught not only what to know but more importantly *how* to know. Perhaps the only thing that AI researchers are in agreement on is the fact that this is a formidable task. Critics of AI point out that nothing even approaching common sense has yet been programmed into any existing computer. Says Stanford's Edward Feigenbaum, "What makes common-sense reasoning so difficult is that you need to know so many facts about the world. How many facts? A million? Some people are trying to codify parts of common sense into a qualitative physics or a qualitative psychology. But who's going to take the time to codify all that? . . . That's why the dream of AI since 1955 or 1956 has been to write a program that can learn from experience. That's the right approach—if only we knew how to do it."[8]

Critics such as Dreyfus don't believe it can be done. To support his conclusion, Dreyfus points out that the notion that a machine can be programmed to learn from experience in a manner similar to a human brain is based on a number of questionable assumptions. All information fed into digital computers must be in *bits*. Can all information essential to the production of intelligent behavior be broken down into bits? As Dreyfus points out, even if all human knowledge could be broken down into a list of discrete facts, the mind boggles at how one might structure the data so that an artificially intelligent computer could immediately access usable information from such a large data base. Dreyfus also criticizes the belief of some AI optimists that the brain processes information in discrete operations by way of some biological equivalent of On/Off switches. This, observes Dreyfus, is a biological assumption that AI researchers have no right to make.[9]

Another problem in creating AI is the imprecision of human thought. Precise numbers and rigorous logic have always typified the workings of the computer, but people deal in vague conceptual gestalts and potentialities rather than clearcut certainties. For example, to teach a computer to recognize the concept *bird* would be an enormous task. The computer would have to learn that some birds fly and some do not; that some are large and some very small; and not only that their shapes vary from the ostrich to the penguin, but that there are real birds as well as pictures of birds, statues of birds, stuffed birds, etc. The problem is that *bird* covers a very broad range of disparate things. In the 1960s an engineer named Lotfi Zadeh at the University of California at Berkeley formalized the rules of an idea he called *fuzzy logic,* and some researchers now believe it may go a long way toward bridging the gap between the computer and the way human beings think. For example, the philosopher Bertrand Russell pointed out that if we try to divide all the men in a village into two mutually exclusive categories—those who shave themselves and so are not shaved by the barber, and those who do not shave themselves and so are shaved by the barber, this seems to take care of categorizing every man in the village until we try to categorize the barber himself. Similarly, someone who is six-foot-eleven is most certainly very tall, but what about someone who is six-foot-four? We might not say that he or she is "very tall," but we wouldn't call the person "not very tall," either.

Not surprisingly, when we try to program computers to deal with even relatively simple problems of everyday life, we come up against the fact that many concepts we consider quite simple are really based on very subtle and complex rules.

Fuzzy logic allows objects to have "degrees of membership" in various categories. If a computer were programmed to tell its owner whether it was "a nice day for a picnic," it would have to be programmed to understand that sometimes a temperature of 78 degrees F. would be considered "nice" and other times it wouldn't—depending, for example, on humidity or whether or not it was raining. In other words, 78 degrees would have to have a degree of membership in the gestalt that the computer understood as "a nice day for a picnic."

Zadeh's original work remained unused until the eary 1970s, when a control engineer named Abe Mamdani at Queen Mary College, London, set about programming a computer to run a kiln. At first he modeled his program on the then-extant learning systems. He quickly discovered that the computer was severely limited by this method. He did not meet with success until he discovered Zadeh's ideas and devised a system that incorporated more fuzzy terms. Instead of simply teaching the computer a rule, such as "When the pressure gets too high, turn the heat down quickly," Mamdani and his colleagues had to teach the computer that "high pressure" had a degree of membership in the rule "to turn the heat down," but the other factors also came into play. They completed their work on the program, incorporating fuzzy logic into their design, and successfully programmed the computer to run the kiln. Indeed, such a computer now runs a cement kiln for F. L. Smith and Company in Copenhagen, and other researchers around the world are also focusing attention on Zadeh's approach.[10]

Still, not many have embodied Zadeh's logic in their approaches. Hubert Dreyfus, for example, has accused Zadeh's concept itself of being a little too "fuzzy."[11]

Many researchers are still unrestrictedly confident that AI is not only possible but inevitable. In *The Fifth Generation,* Edward Feigenbaum and writer Pamela McCorduck sidestep the *hows* of artificial intelligence and focus instead on what they feel are even more crucial concerns. They are convinced that a new breed of artificially intelligent computers is going to be available in the very near future. They predict that such computers will need no special programming languages but will speak to us directly. We will not even have to be very specific about what we require from them. Because they will have reasoning power, they will be able to tease the information out of us. Moreover, they will function a thousand times faster than today's machines, and because they will be hooked into a vast information network, they will be able to use the knowledge of centuries to solve problems. In short, they will be a new order of intelligence.[12]

Feigenbaum and McCorduck do not question the certainty of all of this. They are more concerned with two other issues. The first is the extent to which they feel the new breed of computers will alter civilization as we know it. To begin with, they believe that the fifth generation of computers will be inexpensive and reliable enough to permeate every level of our lives—our offices, our factories, our restaurants, our shops, our farms, and our homes and cars.

More importantly, because they will be powerful extensions of our intellect, the new breed of computers will propel us years into the future, developing unexplored fields of knowledge and contributing actively to the progress of human society.

According to Feigenbaum and McCorduck, the magnitude of change that they will effect in the world will be far beyond anything we can yet conceive. Knowledge will be the new wealth of nations.

In the end, the race to complete the fifth generation of computers is a strange one, for no one yet even knows what is needed to cross the finish line. Not only do the major competing teams disagree with one another, but numerous factions within each team are also involved in animated debate. One area of agreement among all of the participants is that the fifth generation of computers must incorporate a new type of architecture known as *massive parallelism,* the subject of the next chapter.

# Massive Parallelism

The fundamental architecture of most current computers traces its origin back to work that John von Neumann first set down in the 1940s. Von Neumann's proposed basic computer design consisted of two main parts—a processor to perform mathematical or logical operations, and a memory to store data and instructions—connected by a single electronic pathway. Although this basic design works fine for many computer tasks, researchers have realized that it also has quite definite limits. Extremely complex problems, such as modeling weather systems or simulating the behavior of atomic systems, may literally require years of computer time on such machines, which makes the solving of certain problems too time-consuming and costly to perform. Similarly, researchers are in the embarrassing position of finding that the smarter they make such von Neumann machines, and the more information they provide them with to solve their tasks, the slower such computers become.

Even the most expert systems turn out to be little more than idiot savants, capable of solving problems in only one narrow area. This stricture becomes especially acute when such a computer is asked to perform more than one task at a time. For example, in one recent experiment, a motorized cart was equipped with a computerized vision system and was asked to negotiate its way through a hall filled with obstacles. It was found that it could perform this task quite successfully, but every time it advanced a meter, it had to stop and take a fifteen-minute break to reassess the situation.[1]

One reason for this limitation is the fact that all the information the computer processes must travel over one line, sometimes known as the *von Neumann bottleneck*. Von Neumann himself recognized that parallel processors working in tandem would have an advantage over such systems, but in the pre-chip era of the 1940s, when computers were still constructed out of unwieldy vacuum tubes, such features were impractical.

Some parallel features have been incorporated into the so-called supercomputers of today, a designation for which only sixty-odd computers in the world currently qualify. One of the better known of these is the Cray-2, named after its designer, Seymour Cray. For the past two decades, Cray has almost singlehandedly developed each new generation of supercomputers and contributed significantly to the technological advances that have helped propel the United States to superiority in many areas of research.

Cray's newest creation is one of the fastest supercomputers in the world today. The Cray-2 is so compact and the heat generated by its operations is so intense that it must sit in an aquarium filled with liquid fluorocarbon, like a brain bathed in cerebrospinal fluid, to keep from burning up. Although its central processing unit is only twenty-six inches high and thirty-eight inches long—compared to the nine-foot length of its predecessor—the Cray-2 can perform an astounding 1.2 billion operations a second. To accomplish this feat, Cray has incorporated into his brainchild four processors that run together.

---

Most standard computers are based on a design that consists of a single processor and memory connected by a middle component or bus. In the past, most of the advances that were made in computer-processing ability were effected by continually upgrading this single processor. However, most researchers agree that a limit has been reached by following this approach. Many believe that, instead of a single processor, the supercomputers of the future will be based on a design consisting of many processors and memories operating in parallel.

# Now

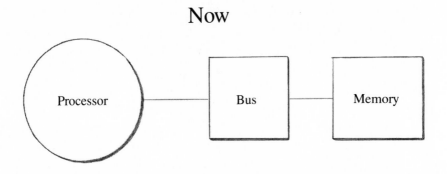

# Future?

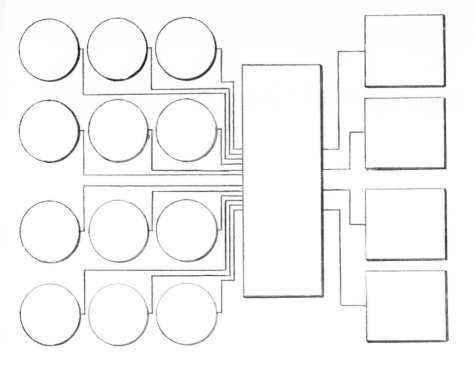

However, even the Cray-2 falls far short of the computational capabilities many researchers are aiming for in the new generation of machines. David Shaw, a computer scientist at Columbia University, is currently at work on a supercomputer that will employ a design quite different from Cray's. Instead of having four powerful processors working in tandem, Shaw's machine will be an interlocking network of a million weaker processors in a pyramidlike structure, topped by a few, more powerful processors. The thinking behind this machine—called Non-Von 4 because of its radical departure from von Neumann–type computers—is that many little brains working together are better than just a few extremely powerful brains working together.

The hope is that such massive parallelism will result in computers with both vastly increased speed and heightened computational power. The idea for hooking so many processors together was actually proposed in 1967 by Jacob Schwartz, director of the computer science division at NYU's Courant Institute of Mathematical Sciences, but was not practical at that time because computer chips were still too expensive. As Schwartz points out, a machine the size of Non-Von 4 "would have cost a billion dollars then."[2] It has only been in the past decade, when advances in technology have made chips more affordable, that researchers have returned to plans of constructing such parallel processors.

Massive parallelism is not without its new breed of possibly massive problems. As Shaw has said, if you have a million processors, the chances are reasonably high that in any given operation one of them is going to fail. This problem is especially critical in Non-Von 4's design because, due to the pyramid or treelike arrangement of its processors, if one fails, all those branching out beneath it will also be knocked out. To compensate for this, Shaw plans to put spare processing elements in the machine to permit it to reroute signals around a bad circuit, but he concedes that other problems may come into play. For example, programming a system with thousands upon thousands of computing elements could prove to be a nightmare. States Shaw, "Programming this kind of machine is going to be so different that there's going to be a tremendous relearning process."[3] No one has yet even tried to write software to tell such systems what to do because no massively parallel computer has yet been completed. Without the opportunity to study different kinds of parallel processors in operation, no one yet knows which design, if any, will prove to be the most effective. Unlike the standard von Neumann computer, which has only one possible architecture, the way that thousands and even millions of individual processors can be interconnected is theoretically infinite. Shaw's plan, to arrange them in a binary tree, is only one solution. Currently dozens of other research groups are working on other variants of the parallel-processing problem.

For example, W. Daniel Hillis and his colleagues at the MIT Artificial-Intelligence Laboratory are working on another solution, a model they've named the Connection Machine. Hillis is basing his design on the concept of cellular automata. Instead of arranging all of the million separate processors that will make up his machine in a binary tree, Hillis is arranging them so that each processor is ultimately connected to every other processor in the array, not unlike the way that every neuron in the human brain is ultimately connected to every other neuron. Hillis hopes to make his Connection Machine capable of *semantic-network* reasoning—a machine that thinks in relatively the same way that humans think.

Not everyone shares Hillis's optimism. Schank believes that massive parallelism by itself will provide increased speed, but it will offer no more insight into the way that learning or common sense or any of the truly fundamental functions of AI operate than conventional von Neumann computers working at slower speeds have.

AI pioneer Allen Newell of Carnegie-Mellon disagrees. He believes that not only will new architectures and new ways of programming trigger new ways of thinking about intelligence, but massive parallelism might also help bridge the gap between AI and cognitive psychology, on one hand, and neuroscience, on the other. As Newell points out, from the 1940s to the 1960s there were substantial efforts to build *neural nets,* computer systems modeled on the human nervous system.[4] In the years since then, the idea of constructing these neural nets lost momentum, and AI research went off in an entirely different direction. Now, however, with the resurgence of interest in parallelism and the formation of a school of "new connectionists," the notion of modeling computer designs on the patterns inherent in the human brain has returned, and Newell believes that this renaissance may offer new insights into the fundamental laws that govern thinking entities in general— both human and nonhuman.

*Part V*

---

# THE UNORTHODOX UNIVERSE

One of the ironies of science is that researchers in all fields seem to enjoy deciding who in their ranks is going beyond the acceptable bounds of invention in the pursuit of scientific knowledge—who is guilty of inventing something that belongs more properly in the realm of pseudoscience or even religion. As the late philosopher Herbert Marcuse once noted, science is not value free, and although developing "pancake theories" for the origin of the galaxies and dividing up the first trillion-trillionths of a second of the creation of the universe may be acceptable, certain ponderings on other matters are not.

In this section we will cover recent theories and points of view offered by various researchers that are not accepted by the scientific community at large and are considered heretical by most. These unorthodox explorations include questions about the possible extraterrestrial origin of life, questions about mysterious forces that may work above and beyond the accepted processes of evolution, and even questions about God and the human soul.

# Wholeness and
# the Implicate Order

A number of the tenets of quantum theory depart radically from the classical deterministic and Newtonian view of the universe. For example, according to Heisenberg's uncertainty principle, it is impossible to know certain pairs of properties of a particle simultaneously. Two such properties are the position and the momentum of an electron, which, according to the uncertainty principle, simply cannot exist at the same time. Our inability to know both the position and momentum of an electron simultaneously is not due to technological limitations. Quantum theory asserts that there is something intrinsic to the nature of the electron that makes knowing both at the same time impossible.

A second radical assertion made in quantum theory is that it is meaningless to describe a phenomenon without taking its observer into account. In other words, instead of believing in a universe in which reality is objective and can be viewed dispassionately, quantum theory adopted the point of view that the observer and the observed are somehow fundamentally and inextricably linked.

A third departure is the notion of *nonlocality*. According to quantum theory, when certain atomic systems divide in two, measurements performed on one part will affect the behavior of the other part, regardless of its location in space and time. Einstein believed that such a state of affairs violated relativity's ban on any signal propagating faster than the speed of light. Other physicists hold that nonlocality is the solution and that, in the subatomic landscape, everyday notions of objects existing in precise locations simply break down. Whatever the case, recent developments have shown that measurements made on such paired particles *are* correlated, even when the particles are separated by comparatively large distances. Whether this means faster-than-light signaling is occurring is still highly controversial.

In 1951 physicist David Bohm published his now classic *Quantum Theory*, which many consider to be the standard text on orthodox quantum physics. Almost immediately after its publication, Bohm became troubled by many of the apparent contradictions inherent in the theory and set about finding ways to resolve them.

One of the first problems Bohm had with quantum theory was that it provided no clear way of understanding movement or process. One could discuss an observation and then another, but to Bohm, quantum theory was incapable of accurately describing motion or explaining in a substantial way how one moment in time was connected to the next. After the publication of *Quantum Theory*, he sent off copies to Einstein, Bohr, and Wolfgang Pauli. He received no answer from Bohr, an enthusiastic answer from Pauli, and an invitation from Einstein to discuss the book, which he eagerly accepted. It was in his discussions with Einstein that his new view began to coalesce.

According to quantum theory, the state of a particle at any given instant can be represented by a mathematical quantity known as a wave function. Each wave function is determined as the result of an observation, and the only way to describe the trajectory of a particle in motion is as a series or linear combination of wave functions, each one collapsing and being replaced by another at the end of each observation. After his discussion with Einstein, Bohm concluded that the wave functions had to be connected in some manner, in order for each to be able to converge and somehow to give rise to the next. He therefore postulated the existence of a connecting principle he called the *quantum potential*.

It was clear to Bohm that, if it existed, the quantum potential belonged to a realm outside of the current explanatory principles. For example, in pairs of particles that remained correlated even after they were widely separated in space and time, the wave function describing one of the pairs of particles appeared to be connected to the wave function of the other. Otherwise the two particles would not appear to communicate instantaneously, regardless of their proximity or distance. It was this realization that made Bohm start to consider that there was a region that, indeed, existed beyond space and time. He called this transcendent realm the *implicate order.*[1]

In *Wholeness and the Implicate Order,* published in 1980, Bohm provides a metaphor for visualizing how the implicate order might explain such beyond-space-and-time connections between particles. As he suggests, imagine an aquarium in which a fish is swimming. Imagine also that there are two television cameras directed at the aquarium, one at the front and one providing a side view. The aquarium and the fish cannot be seen directly but the fish can be viewed on two television screens connected to the two respective cameras. As Bohm points out, each screen will provide a different image of the fish. At any given moment, each image will generally *look* different from the other, but the images will also appear to be related, for they will be executing corresponding movements. The image that is mainly on one screen will pass into the other, and vice versa. For example, when a fish facing one camera turns at a right angle and faces the other camera, the image that was on one screen will be seen to move to the other one. Thus, at all times, the image

---

Bohm believes that subatomic particles do not have an independent existence, but are connected on a higher dimension. In the diagram the fish moves from position A to position B, and this is recorded by cameras 1 and 2. This changes the appearance of the fish in two dimensions, but to the third-dimension observer the relationship of the changes is obvious. Bohm suggests that perhaps subatomic particles are similarly connected at a higher multidimensional level.

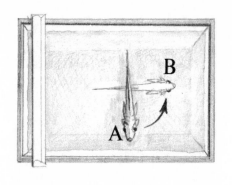

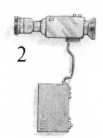

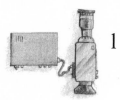

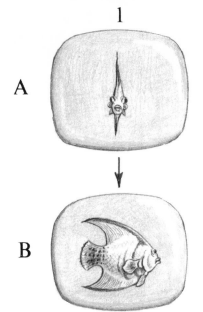

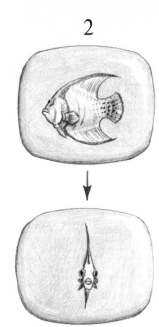

content on each screen will correlate with and reflect that of the other.

Bohm states, "Of course, we know that the two images do not refer to independently existent though interacting actualities (in which, for example, one image could be said to 'cause' related changes in the other). Rather, they refer to a single actuality, which is the common ground of both (and this explains the correlation of images without the assumption that they causally affect each other). This actuality is of higher dimensionality than are the separate images on the screens. To put it differently, the images on the screens are two-dimensional *projections* (or facets) of a three-dimensional reality. In some sense, this three-dimensional reality holds these two-dimensional projectsions within it. Yet, since these projections exist only as abstractions, the three-dimensional reality *is* neither of these, but rather it is something else, something of a nature beyond both." [2]

Bohm believes that the nonlocal, noncausal relationship between the twin particles produced by certain subatomic processes may be understood by extension of the metaphor above. That is to say, we may regard each of the particles constituting the system as a projection of a "higher-dimensional" reality, rather than as a separate entity. The two-dimensional image on the television screen becomes the analogue for our own apparent three-dimensional reality. And the television studio or higher reality, in which the two particles are actually different facets of the same multidimensional something, is the implicate order.

Bohm feels that the introduction of the notion of an implicate order into physics also helps explain how various successive wave functions of any given particle are related. In Bohm's view, the appearance and disappearance of consecutive wave functions can now be considered as a constant series of unfoldings and *enfoldings* in and out of the backdrop of the implicate order. [3]

The concept of an enfolded order first struck Bohm in the 1960s, while he was watching a television program. In the program he saw a specially designed jar at the Royal Institution containing a rotating cylinder and a narrow space filled with glycerin. As Bohm watched, the cylinder was turned by a handle at the top, and a drop of ink was placed in the glycerin. The turning of the cylinder caused the droplet to smear into nothingness and to become enfolded in the glycerin. However, when the handle turned back the other way, the original drop of ink reappeared as if it were unfolded from the glycerin and regained its original shape. This gave Bohm a metaphor for the sort of process that he was trying to describe, demonstrating how order may appear to be absent but may nevertheless be implied and ready to appear under the right conditions. He began to view the position and momentum of the electron as two drops of ink dropped into the glycerin at different stages of turning: If the position was clearly observed, the momentum was still smeared, whereas by the time the turning had progressed far enough for the momentum to become clear, the position had become smeared.[4] In this sense, the implicate order becomes a realm in which all thing-events are enfolded in a wholeness or unity that underlies the explicate world of separate things and events.

However, if the actual reality of a particle such as an electron is enfolded in some sort of higher and multidimensional implicate order, and if when we perceive such properties as momentum and spin we are actually glimpsing only facets of the electron's total reality, we may ask: What else lies hidden enfolded within the implicate order? Bohm answers: "What is implied by this proposal is that what we call empty space contains an immense background of energy, and that matter as we know it is a small, 'quantized' wavelike excitation on top of this background. . . . It is being suggested here, then, that what we perceive through the senses as empty space is actually the plenum, which is the ground for the existence of everything, including ourselves. The things that appear to our senses are derivative forms and their true meaning can be seen only when we consider the plenum, in which they are generated and sustained, and into which they must ultimately vanish."[5]

Following this tack, he makes a number of speculations. One is that black holes may actually be portals into the plenum, or cosmic background of energy. Another is that what we perceive as our universe is but one of many universes unfolding out of other facets of the implicate order. Bohm even feels that his notion of the implicate order may offer important insights into other phenomena, such as plant and animal life.

He notes that in terms of the implicate order, inanimate matter maintains itself in a continual process very similar to that observed in the growth of plants. As a plant is formed, maintained, and dissolved by the exchange of matter and energy with its environment, Bohm points out that there is really no clear distinction between what is alive and what is not. Clearly, a carbon dioxide molecule that crosses a cell boundary into a leaf does not suddenly come alive, nor does a molecule of oxygen suddenly die when it is expelled in the breath. Rather, life itself has to be regarded as belonging in some sense to a totality that includes both plant and environment. This idea is reminiscent of a comment made by Alan Watts: "Spring does not become summer: there is spring, and then there is summer. Likewise firewood does not become ashes, nor the living body a corpse. This is how reality appears to one who knows that only the present is real."

For Bohm, a forest is constituted of trees that are continually dying and being replaced by new ones. If it is considered on a long timescale, the forest may likewise be regarded as a continuously existent but slowly changing entity. In this sense, different trees that appear and vanish in the forest are like different properties of the electron or different droplets of ink in the cylinder filled with glycerin, and both life and inanimate matter can be viewed as different facets of the totality enfolded in the implicate order.

If life is somehow "implicit" in the universe, if the design of an organism is somehow enfolded in the cosmic background of energy, even when the organism does not materially exist in our own observable universe, it must be concluded that the implicate order is a warehouse of infinite designs, the blueprints for virtually everything from quarks to galaxies, from snowflakes to the human brain. Even consciousness itself, Bohm suggests, may be derived from the implicate order in the sense that, in each and every moment of awareness, thought seems to constantly unfold and enfold to form a continuity very similar to the unfolding and enfolding of the wave functions that constitute a particle's trajectory.

Bohm believes that the workings of consciousness and the phenomena encountered in quantum physics are not fundamentally different. Both, he asserts, display their own sort of creativity and insight because both have sprung from the common ground of the implicate order. Thus, Bohm concludes, nature itself is alive, all the way to its depths, and displays a deep intentionality, creativity, and purposiveness. But at this point, he adds, it may not be satisfactory to continue to use the term *nature*. As he states, "It could equally well be called Idealism, Spirit, Consciousness. The separation of the two—matter and spirit—is an abstraction."[6]

The overview of Bohm's current thinking is that we cannot understand the phenomena of physics, the thing-events of the explicate order, without recognizing that they are part of a totality or wholeness that includes the multidimensional higher ground of the implicate order. However, he does not presume to assert that even this wholeness is the "totality of all that is." As he states at the end of his book, "We regard even this ground as a mere stage, in the sense that there could in principle be an infinity of further development beyond it."[7]

Although Bohm has retained the respect of his colleagues for the significance of his early work, many have been reluctant to accept his more recent ideas and believe that no further explanation of the apparent correlation between twin particles is necessary. In a recent article on Bohm's work, science writer Robert Temple added, "Although physicists of his own age are unlikely to want to look

into the challenge he poses, as they have now shown such reluctance to do so for more than thirty years, younger scientists have
been showing increased interest in his ideas."[8]

In spite of the lack of receptivity to his ideas, Bohm continues to
refine the mathematics of his theory, remaining convinced that
quantum physics cannot be considered a whole unto itself but
points to something outside of itself. Such a point of view recalls
the words of G. Spencer Brown, that we can "eventually construct
the universe, in every detail and potentiality, as you know it now;
but then, again, what you will construct will not be all, for by the
time you will have reached what now is, the universe will have
expanded into a new order to contain what will then be. . . . Thus
the world, whenever it appears as a physical universe, must always
seem to us, its representatives, to be playing a kind of hide-and-
seek with itself. What is revealed will be concealed, but what is
concealed will again be revealed."[9]

# Did Man Really Fall to Earth?

In 1924, Russian biochemist Alexander I. Oparin theorized that the Earth's first oceans were a hot, dilute brew of simple molecules. He further suggested that it was the constant bombardment of this primordial soup by lightning that sparked connections between these simple inorganic molecules and knitted them together into larger, nonbiologically produced organic molecules. Over the course of millions of years, these organic molecules were in turn knitted together into still larger structures—primitive proteins and nucleic acids—until they became the self-replicating systems we know as life.

In the 1950s, Stanley L. Miller and Harold C. Urey of the University of Chicago, as a test of Oparin's model, tried to synthesize organic compounds in the lab, mimicking conditions thought to have existed on the young Earth. Miller and Urey, in their now famous experiment, took sterilized water, added an atmosphere of hydrogen, ammonia, and methane, and then subjected the mixture to continuous electrical discharge for one week. At the end of the week they discovered that they had produced several simple amino acids. In the thirty years since their landmark discovery, other scientists, using more involved procedures, have produced more sophisticated organic substances—longer chains of amino acids; ribose and glucose sugars; and even nucleoside phosphates, the precursors of DNA. Most scientists interested in biochemical evolution believed that if such complex substances could be so created in such short spans of time, it was not implausible that, given billions of years, life could have indeed evolved out of the primordial soup.

Dr. Chandra Wickramasinghe of University College at Cardiff, Wales, and Sir Fred Hoyle reject this orthodox view of the origin of life on the grounds that it is "too improbable." In *Evolution from Space* and *Diseases from Space,* they set forth the idea that life did not begin in a primordial soup but actually fell to the Earth from space. Although Hoyle, the father of the steady-state theory of the origin of the universe, is an eminent scientist respected by his peers for his earlier work, this recent proposal has not been met with enthusiasm.

Wickramasinghe and Hoyle arrived at their conclusion using the following line of reasoning: A living cell has a chain of amino acids, of which there are twenty different kinds. The function of these amino acids is dependent upon one thousand to two thousand highly specialized enzymes. They postulate that, for an enzyme to work in the amino acid chain, assuming its correct configuration in space, at least twenty to thirty key amino acids must be "right." The probability of this happening by chance is approximately $10^{-40}$. Thus, in their view, the probability that a thousand different enzymes configured by accident to form life is $10^{40,000}$ to 1.

Wickramasinghe and Hoyle claim recent discoveries by paleobiologists support their hypothesis. When Oparin first proposed his model, it was generally believed that life first appeared on the Earth about 600 million years ago, just before the Cambrian period. However, in the late 1970s, Stanley M. Awramik of the University of California at Santa Barbara discovered sedimentary rocks in Western Australia, containing fossils of microbial life 3.5 billion years old. Furthermore, the fossils were of a microbial life form so complex that life must have already been well along at the time that they were preserved.[1] Given that the age of the Earth is estimated to be about 4.6 billion years, this means that terrestrial life did not have billions of years to evolve, but a significantly shorter span of time, thus increasing Wickramasinghe's and Hoyle's already improbable odds.

Wickramasinghe and Hoyle assert that prestellar molecular clouds, such as those in the Orion Nebula, and not the primordial soup appear to be the most natural cosmic cradles of life.[2] Hoyle believes that, despite the microwave background radiation permeating the cosmos, the universe is eternal. Given the limited timescale of the Earth's existence, Wickramasinghe and Hoyle believe that only the interstellar dust clouds of space could provide the unlimited time necessary for evolution.

Secondly, they make the assertion that spectroscopic analysis of interstellar clouds reveals the possible existence of vast quantities of complex organic substances. Following this train of thought, Wickramasinghe and Hoyle suggest that not only did interstellar debris rain down on the primitive Earth and seed the first life here but it is still raining down. They propose that this perpetual "infection" from outer space may be responsible for the periodic and abrupt appearance throughout history of various diseases, such as the plague that devastated Athens in 429 B.C. and another that killed two-thirds of the population of China in 312 A.D.[3] This "infection" also may explain why, throughout history, comets have been so often associated with times of foreboding and doom.

Concerning the considerable opposition to Wickramasinghe's and Hoyle's theories, many biologists do not believe that the enzyme system of a cell was put together by random combinations of amino acids. It is generally accepted that the enzyme system itself evolved from much simpler systems, meaning that the probabilities figured by Hoyle and Wickramasinghe may be based on a completely incorrect line of reasoning. H.N.V. Temperley, formerly of the Department of Applied Mathematics, University of Wales, believes that life could have evolved from a *proto-ribosome* with as few as one or two enzymes. Employing generally accepted theories of statistical mechanics, he has shown that as many as $10^{60}$ amino-acid configurations could have been "tried out" in the primordial soup, and given the simpler structure of this proto-ribosome, he feels that life could have occurred by accident without the invocation of either divine creation or the appearance of proto-life from interstellar space.[4]

Similarly, Robert Shapiro criticizes Wickramasinghe and Hoyle on the grounds that they have not properly substantiated many of the details of their claims. For example, they claim that a study of the infrared spectra of an interstellar cloud reveals evidence of the existence of cellulose, the major component of the woody part of plants and trees. However, Shapiro argues that, in examining the same spectra, he sees no convincing signs of the presence of cellulose in interstellar clouds, concluding that Wickramasinghe and Hoyle are reading too much into the blurry Rorschach of lines of such spectra.[5]

Scientists generally are willing to overlook what many consider to be Hoyle's recent "fringe ideas." However, as with Bohm, he still retains the respect of his peers for his early work.

# Morphogenetic Fields:
# A New Science of Life

Standard biology teaches that animals are machines and that all aspects of their form and function can be expressed in terms of the ordinary forces of nature. The studies of these forces have diversified into a number of approaches, such as physiology, biochemistry, biophysics, genetics, and molecular biology.

In his 1981 book, *A New Science of Life,* biologist Rupert Sheldrake asserts that Western science has misconstrued the workings of the biological world and perhaps a range of nonbiological phenomena as well. "Most biologists," he writes, "take it for granted that living organisms are nothing but complex machines, governed only by the known laws of physics and chemistry. I myself used to share this point of view. But over a period of several years, I came to see that such an assumption is difficult to justify. For, when so little is actually understood, there is an open possibility that at least some of the phenomena of life depend on laws or factors as yet unrecognized by the physical sciences."[1] Sheldrake concedes that, in many respects, all of these approaches have been brilliantly successful. For example, in molecular biology, the discovery of the structure of DNA and the elucidation of the mechanism of protein synthesis are, at first glance, impressive confirmations of the validity of the mechanistic approach. But he also believes that the way form evolves in living systems and perhaps in nonliving systems, such as crystals, is not determined solely by the physical laws and principles that science has so far identified. To explain such puzzles, he suggests the existence of invisible organizing fields he calls *morphogenetic fields*. His assertion has fueled a great deal of criticism in the scientific community.

At first glance Sheldrake is an unlikely rebel. He studied philosophy and history of science at Harvard and received a PhD in biochemistry from his alma mater, Cambridge, where he subsequently became a director of studies in biochemistry and cell biology. In 1974 he was ready to attain the goal of most career scientists, a professorship at the university of his choice, but instead decided he wanted to study plants growing in the field instead of isolated in the laboratory. So he moved to India and started working for an International Research Institute in Hyderabad, where he is still a consultant. It was there that he started to consider seriously certain mysteries that biology seemed incapable of explaining, ponderings that ultimately led to the publication of his book. As Sheldrake puts it, "The more I thought about the unsolved problems of biology, the more convinced I became that the conventional approach is unnecessarily restrictive. I started to imagine the possible outlines of a broader science of life."[2]

While Sheldrake concedes that DNA certainly determines protein production, he takes issue with those who believe that it explains all aspects of the genetic program. He cites the obvious enigma presented by the fact that identical copies of DNA are passed on to all cells in a developing embryo, and yet somehow, something tells different cells to develop differently. What is it? Sheldrake asks. There are numerous other similar mysteries. For instance, developing systems are also somehow able to regulate themselves. If a part of a developing organism is removed, the organism is able to regulate itself and to continue to develop until a more-or-less normal structure is produced. The classic demonstration of this phenomenon was provided in the 1890s by the German biologist Hans Driesch, in his experiments on sea urchin embryos. Driesch discovered that when one of the cells of a very young embryo, at the two-celled stage, was killed, the remaining cell gave rise not to half a sea urchin but to a smaller, complete sea urchin. Similarly, small but complete organisms continue to develop after the destruction of any one, two, or three cells of embryos at the four-celled stage. Conversely, the fusion of two young sea urchin embryos will result in the development of a giant sea urchin.[3]

Sheldrake points out a similar puzzle in the ability of many organisms to regenerate lost limbs and organs. Plants show a great range of regenerative abilities, as do many lower animals. A flat-worm, for example, can be cut into several pieces, and each can regenerate into a complete worm. One particular striking example of regeneration was reported by the German biologist G. Wolff in 1902. Wolff surgically removed the lens from a newt's eye and discovered that within thirty days a new lens had regenerated from the iris of the newt. What is remarkable is that Wolff had deliberately chosen a type of mutilation that could not have occurred by accident, and thus the regenerative capacity could not have evolved through natural selection. Once again, Sheldrake wants to know *what* takes the DNA blueprint and determines which annex of the building to reconstruct, as it were. Blueprints don't just grow into structures without builders to interpret them, and Sheldrake was troubled that molecular biology had no real explanation for this process. The characteristic form and organization of living systems is governed, Sheldrake argues, by more than just a genetic blueprint. It is also governed by a morphogenetic blueprint, a new type of physical field with measurable physical effects.

Sheldrake uses an analogy to help illustrate his thesis. Imagine a man who has been studying a radio. If the man had no knowledge of electromagnetic radiation, he might conclude that the radio's components—its circuits, wires, and transistors—were all that were involved in the radio's operation. Any alterations he made—changing the tuning or the set's components—would produce effects entirely consistent with this conclusion. Yet, for the radio to work, it still has to pick up and to amplify electromagnetic transmissions from a distant station, even though our imaginary man has no knowledge or awareness of those transmissions.

Sheldrake thinks that biologists are in a similar position. They believe that form and function are completely due to genetic inheritance—the radio's hardware—and have completely overlooked the fact that morphogenetic fields—the radio wave transmissions—might also be an integral part of explaining the radio's operations.

To support this thesis, Sheldrake calls upon some even more intriguing puzzles than the ones already delineated in the field of embryology. One involves a mystery encountered recently by a research team headed by biologist Mae Wan Ho of the Open University at Walton, England. Ho's team took fruit flies from ordinary stock and exposed them to ether, thus causing some of the flies to become bithorax mutants, developing four wings instead of two. In the first generation of exposed fruit flies, 4 percent developed double sets of wings and 96 percent remained normal. The researchers then let those flies mate at random and exposed the next generation of eggs to an identical amount of ether. In this generation, about 8 percent became bithorax. The researchers continued to repeat the process, and with each succeeding generation of fruit flies, more and more were born with the bithorax mutations—10 percent, 12 percent, and so on, until the team reached a point where 40 or 50 percent of a generation was showing up with bithorax mutations in response to the ether.

Ho interpreted these findings as arising from some sort of Lamarckian effect in the cytoplasm. (Lamarck, it may be remem-

---

Fruit fly eggs being treated with ether as Dr. Sheldrake looks on. By the twentieth repetition many more mutated individuals were found than was predicted by standard biological theories. Sheldrake believes that certain nonphysical fields that are as yet unrecognized by science and that he calls "morphogenetic fields" may be responsible.

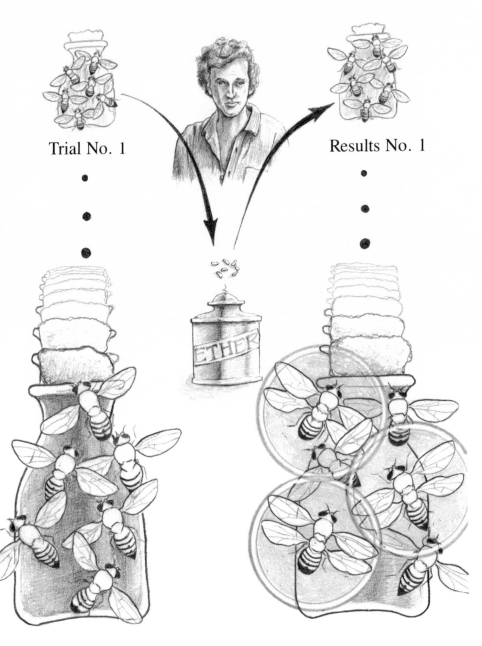

Trial No. 1

Results No. 1

Trial No. 20

Results No. 20

bered, believed that acquired characteristics could be inherited and proposed this as an evolutionary mechanism. Neo-Darwinians, however, do not accept such a view.) After Ho's team had been performing this experiment for some time, they took a group of fruit fly eggs from regular stock—flies whose ancestors had never been exposed to ether—and performed the test on them. The striking result was that in the first generation 10 percent were bithorax. In the next generation, 20 percent. Even assuming the existence of some sort of Lamarckian effect, such high percentages should not have occurred in a completely unrelated group of fruit fly eggs taken from regular stock. Sheldrake points out, too, that being bithorax hinders the fruit flies, as opposed to helping them, so there should be no natural selection in favor of such mutations.[4]

Sheldrake believes that such phenomena suggest the existence of morphogenetic fields that are influencing the structure of the fruit flies above and beyond their own genetic blueprints. He feels that it is these fields that also direct such genetic programs as the self-regulation of embryos and the abilities of many living systems to regenerate. As to where such field structures come from, Sheldrake says, "The answer suggested is that they are derived from the morphogenetic fields assiciated with previous similar systems: the morphogenetic fields of all past systems become *present* to any subsequent similar systems by a cumulative influence which acts across both space *and time.*"[5]

Sheldrake thinks that the existence of such fields might also account for the appearance of almost identical living structures in widely disparate lines of evolution. He points to the fact that there is a species of Mediterranean dryland snail that has a shell nearly identical in shape and structure with those of snails of other genera. Similarly, identical wing patterns can occur in quite different families of butterflies. In fact, Sheldrake proposes that the uncanny repetition of form that pervades all life—the tentacles of *Hydra* and the arms of starfish, the feathers of all species of birds, the fact that all trees have leaves, and even the fact that on the microscopic level all tissues contain thousands or millions of copies of a few basic cells—might be due to the ability of one species to "tune in," to some extent, to another species's morphogenetic field. Sheldrake also believes that it is a combination of the influence of morphogenetic fields and genetic selection that enables random mutations to become hereditary characteristics throughout an entire species.

Further, Sheldrake proposes that organisms may be able to tune in not only to each other's structures but to each other's behavior as well. He points, for example, to certain mysterious results in studies of animal behavior. In 1920 Harvard psychologist William McDougall began a series of experiments systematically training related generations of rats to perform a particular task. McDougall placed rats in a specially constructed water maze from which they could escape only by swimming to an unlighted gangway. If they chose to swim toward a lighted gangway, they received an electric shock. McDougall then measured their rate of learning by counting the number of errors they made before learning to swim straight to the unlighted gangway.

What was strange about McDougall's findings was that, even though the task did not change, *later generations of rats learned more quickly than generations preceding them.* This effect persisted even when he bred only the slowest-learning rats in each generation. In fact, in twenty-two generations of rats, McDougall observed an almost *tenfold* increase in their rate of learning. Following McDougall's findings, studies were set up in Scotland and Australia to duplicate the experiment, and in both, the first generation of rats learned almost as quickly as McDougall's last generation. Some of the rats even "learned" the task immediately, thus avoiding being shocked at all.[6] (It is important to note that the rat experiment cited took over a decade to complete and such results have not been reported in similar shorter-term experiments.) Sheldrake believes this occurred because the first generation of rats established a morphogenetic field for the specific behavior being learned. That field then helped guide the behavior of subsequent generations, making it easier for them to learn the task through a process Sheldrake calls *morphic resonance.*

If this seems difficult to fathom, Sheldrake points out that the process by which behavior becomes instinct is no less mysterious. Spiders can spin intricate webs without ever having learned how; European cuckoos, who are hatched and reared by birds of other species, nonetheless know when to migrate and where to go to reach their ancestral winter habitats in southern Africa; and sheep dogs, which have been trained and selected over many generations for their ability to round up sheep, are now born with an innate tendency toward such behavior. Sheldrake proposes that his theory is a "hypothesis of repetition"; if things happen once in a certain way, it will be easier for them to happen the same way a second time because of the influence of the morphogenetic field thus established.

What implications does the hypothesis of repetition have for human behavior? ARE WE ALL ON THE SAME WAVELENGTH? asks a headline for an article in the *Times* of London on Sheldrake's work.[7] Are children able to learn to ride bicycles or to roller skate more quickly now than they were at the beginning of the century? Will tomorrow's children be quicker at learning to play video games or to operate computers than today's generation? Sheldrake thinks it's a good possibility. He cites an article in *Nature* reporting that the average IQ of American children has increased .36 point per year since 1947.[8] This does not necessarily indicate we are all getting more intelligent. States Sheldrake, "Intelligence is not an easy thing to define. I think it basically indicates that we are all getting better at taking IQ tests over and over."[9] Critics also argue that .36 is a very small increase and could be explained by environmental factors.

Nonetheless, Sheldrake argues that the notion seems supported by the fact that the average IQ of Japanese children is six points ahead of the mean score of white American children. One explanation of the steadily increasing IQ of the Japanese is postwar urbanization and recent improvements in health, welfare, and education. But in the United States similar changes occurred early in the century. Why should IQ only now be increasing so rapidly? Are such increases dependent not on environment but on morphogenetic fields gathering momentum? Again, critics suggest that environmental factors are the simpler explanation.

Sheldrake does not limit his hypothesis of repetition to living systems. He believes that there is evidence that the form and inherited characteristics of nonliving systems, such as the formation of crystals, are also governed by morphogenetic fields. He refers to certain puzzles in this area uncovered by other investigators. For example, in their 1961 book *Crystals and Crystal Growing,* A. Holden and P. Singer relate an unusual incident that happened at a company involved in growing single, large crystals of ethylene diamine tartrate. For three years the company tried to develop a monohydrate form of the crystals but was unable to develop such a form. So, instead, they concentrated on growing anhydrous ethylene diamine tartrate, the crystals of which they would then ship to another factory, where they would be cut and polished for industrial use.

A year after the company opened, the crystals in the growing tanks suddenly started to grow badly. A new and less desirable crystalline structure started to manifest. As it turned out, it was the monohydrate form that the company had previously tried so hard to create. Once the monohydrate form made its appearance in reality, it started to appear everywhere, even on the surface of the crystals waiting to be cut at the other factory.

The conventional explanation for the fact that substances usually crystallize more easily after they have been crystallized for the first time is that *seed* crystals travel microscopically through the air and infect other crystals. There can be no doubt that this happens in some instances and over a short distance, but Holden and Singer—in ideas that foreshadow Sheldrake's—feel that more credence should be given to the notion that the preference for a crystal to take a certain form is facilitated by the mere fact that it has crystallized that way before. They even go so far as to suggest that on other planets, types of crystals that are common on Earth may not yet have appeared. As they state, "Perhaps in our own world many other possible solid species are still unknown, not because their ingredients are lacking, but simply because suitable seeds have not yet put in an appearance."[10] Sheldrake agrees that this is a possibility.

As to what morphogenetic fields might consist of and what energy might be involved in making them operate, Sheldrake states, "They are comparable to other fields spoken of in physics, like a gravitational field or a magnetic field. They are invisible and undetectable by our senses, but they have the property of being spatial patterns and are detectable through their effects, much the same as a gravitational field is invisible and only detectable through its effects."[11]

In a recent article Sheldrake added that he feels morphogenetic fields are also *nonenergetic*—that they have a nonlocal character and are able to act outside of time and space. If they involved a transfer of energy, he holds that it would not be possible for them to have their nonlocal character. In other words, it would not be possible for the form of snail genera in distant geographic places to cut across space and time and to influence the form of a Mediterranean dryland snail living today.[12]

Sheldrake's notion that morphogenetic fields are nonlocal and act across space and time is very similar to an idea put forth by Bohm—that the world of separate and isolated thing-events, the explicate order, can be understood only if we posit the existence of an implicate order, a realm in which all thing-events are "enfolded" in a total wholeness or unity that is also nonlocal. Bohm believes that at this implicate level there are energies at work that are so subtle we have not detected them or do not think of them as energy. Yet he feels these subtle energies have a formative influence on less subtle levels.[13]

In comparing his concept of the implicate order with Sheldrake's theory of morphogenetic fields, Bohm states, "The major difference is that the implicate order is more general. It does not require morphogenetic theory, but it may have room to explain one. . . . The implicate order can be thought of as a ground beyond time, a totality, out of which each moment is projected into the explicate order. For every moment that is projected out into the explicate there would be another movement in which that moment would be injected or 'introjected' back into the implicate order. Now, if you have a large number of repetitions of this process, you'll start to build up a fairly constant component to this series of projection and injection. That is, a fixed disposition would become established. The point is that, via this process, past forms would tend to be repeated or replicated in the present, and that is very similar to what Sheldrake calls a morphogenetic field and a morphic resonance."[14]

Bohm believes that part of our current difficulty in arriving at an understanding of such puzzles as the relationship between form and energy is that we do not yet have an adequate understanding of time. As he observes, present-day quantum theory is incapable of really explaining the influence of the past on the present. He states, "Physics doesn't discuss how various successive moments are related, and that's what I say the implicate order is attempting to do."[15]

Not all members of the scientific establishment have found Sheldrake's ideas as compatible with their thinking as Bohm has. When Sheldrake's book first appeared in England, *Nature*, the world's premier scientific journal, commented, "This infuriating tract . . . is the best candidate for burning there has been for many years." Although not as harsh as *Nature*, most scientists do not view Sheldrake's ideas as a proper scientific theory. They argue that it does not satisfy the rules required for a theory to be scientific; the mechanism does not satisfy the known laws of physics. On one hand Sheldrake ignores existing laws, but on the other hand he has not worked out the details of his theory well enough so that others can evaluate it as a coherent structure.

In answer to his critics Sheldrake has offered numerous possible experiments that might prove or disprove his thesis. For example, typewriting is a motor skill around which one could design an experiment to test morphic resonance. As Sheldrake explains, in the United States typewriters have had a standard keyboard layout for so long that the morphogenetic fields associated with their use should strongly bias any experiment with native speakers of English. Attempts to introduce alternative and more efficient keyboard layouts have routinely failed—perhaps because they were up against such a powerful morphogenetic field in the old keyboard layout. As an experiment, American students who had a knowledge of the Russian language but who were unfamiliar with Russian typewriters would be asked to learn to type on them. They could then be tested on typewriters with several different keyboard layouts, all designed so that, regarding relative frequency of letter use, they would be of equivalent difficulty. The question would then be: Would the students learning on typewriters with the standard Russian layout learn faster than those on alternative keyboards?

Similarly, Sheldrake suggests that video games might prove to be a tool to determine the existence of morphic resonance. He points out that the test should be conducted in a place where video games are not widespread as they are in the United States—for example, in India. Sheldrake suggests that a group of children in Bombay could be taught to play a certain game, with their learning rates measured. Then, six months later, a second group of children would be chosen, of similar age, education, and background, from another part of India; and their rates at the same game would be tested. If morphogenetic fields was established, the children in the second group should learn to play the game faster than the children in the first group.

Intrigued by the idea, in October 1982, *New Scientist* offered a £250 prize to the reader who could come up with the best test for Sheldrake's theory.

The judges selected a test devised by Dr. Richard Gentle, a specialist in fluid mechanics at Nottingham University. Gentle prepared two nursery rhymes in Turkish, one a rhyme that had been spoken in Turkey for generations and the other a nonsense rhyme that Gentle made up himself out of Turkish words. The nonsense rhyme followed the same format and rhymed in a manner similar to the real rhyme. Gentle then suggested that schoolchildren be given both rhymes to memorize. According to Sheldrake's theory, the children should be able to memorize the real rhyme—because it had been spoken by other children for generations—faster than the more recent nonsense rhyme.[16]

Critics quickly pointed out that nursery rhymes are not nursery rhymes for nothing and that the genuine Turkish nursery rhyme might catch on, in part, because it was intrinsically more memorable due to an innately pleasant rhythm and meter. To counter this criticism, Shuntaro Tanikawa, a leading Japanese poet, has provided Sheldrake with an old Japanese rhyme and one Tanikawa wrote especially for the test, with the exact same rhythm and meter. So far, Sheldrake reports, test results have been encouraging.

Many scientists are critical of Sheldrake for having written a book and generating publicity about his hypothesis before it has been scientifically proven. His detractors also see him as furthering the cause of such pseudosciences as ESP, clairvoyance, precognition, and other parapsychological phenomena. Lastly, he is also criticized because, unlike Bohm and Hoyle, he does not have a body of impressive previous work to help legitimize his hypothesis.

# Science, God, and the Soul

In this age of rationalism, pragmatism, and technological materialism, it seems strange that scientists continue to entertain such notions as God and religion. In fact, a number of leading scientists continue to probe regions of thought clearly within the borders of the mystical, and with no less fervor than they have probed scientific terrains. The centuries-old saraband of science and religion has not ended yet. It is necessary to note that most scientists do not support these views and find them highly controversial. However, it is intriguing that a few eminent thinkers continue to find in the current advances of science some tentative answers to some of the great metaphysical questions of all time.

In a recent article entitled "Scientists in Search of a Soul," physicist John Gliedman details a case in point. In 1963, the Australian-born physiologist Sir John Eccles won the Nobel Prize for his pioneering research on the synapse of the brain. Now, at the age of seventy-nine, Eccles still strongly defends the ancient religious belief that there is more to us than just matter, that there is, indeed, a ghost in each of our machines. The founding father of modern neurophysiology, Eccles believes that there is a nonmaterial thinking and perceiving self that entered our brain sometime during embryological development or in very early childhood. According to Eccles, it is this nonmaterial presence that makes us distinctly human. He further believes that it functions as a *liaison brain* and actually exerts a certain physical influence on our computerlike and biological brains, causing some neurons to fire and others to remain silent. In this way, Eccles believes, the "soul" functions much the same way as a driver steers a car or a programmer directs a computer, playing an important role in such fundamental human qualities as conscious self-awareness, personal identity, free will, creativity, and even such emotions as love and hate. Eccles further asserts that he believes this nonmaterial self actually survives the death of the physical brain.[1]

René Descartes, the seventeenth-century French philosopher who is generally held responsible for defining the distinction between mind and body, perceived in the distinction the need to determine some mechanism by which the mind and body could interact. In a recent book, *The Wonder of Being Human,* Eccles, along with physiological psychologist Daniel N. Robinson, proposes that they have found such a mechanism. Recent research indicates that a fraction of a second before one makes a voluntary movement, nerve cells in an area of the brain known as the *supplementary motor area* (SMA) begin to fire. What is significant is that no neurophysiological process has currently been found that causes the SMA cells to fire. This has led Eccles and Robinson to reach an unusual conclusion. As Eccles writes: "We have here an irrefutable demonstration that a mental act of intention *initiates* the burst of discharges of a nerve cell." Moreover, as Eccles and Robinson point out, if one repeats a movement until it becomes habitual and can occur without conscious attention, the anticipatory activity in the SMA also fades and then disappears.[2]

It comes as no surprise that Eccles has received strong criticism from numerous other members of the scientific community. In a review of Eccles and Robinson's book, George A. Miller, a professor of psychology at Princeton, expresses the opinion that few researchers will find the authors' conclusions convincing. As he states, "That the cause of activity in SMA cells is not presently known will not persuade them that the cause must be mental. . . . As long as science can continue to advance by observing physical causes and effects, few materialists will be persuaded that mental or spiritual causes are required."[3]

Similarly, while conceding that science has not yet discovered evidence that rules out Eccles's assumption, computer expert Donald MacKay of the University of Keel, in England, stresses that there is still no evidence in favor of it, either. Comparable criticisms come from Daniel Dennet, Tufts University philosopher, who complains that Eccles is not abreast of recent developments in computer science, and Mario Bunge, the distinguished philosopher of science at McGill University, who argues that such claims as Eccles's not only are inconsistent with modern science but actually block its advancement.[4]

Eccles is not completely without his allies. Perhaps the most distinguished philosopher of science of our age, Sir Karl Popper, agrees with Eccles in almost every respect except for the notion of the soul's immortality. Popper is best known for creating the orthodox theory of scientific explanation employed by most working scientists. One of Popper's most faithfully held tenets is that, in order to qualify as scientific, a hypothesis must be falsifiable. In other words, it must be within the realm of possibility to disprove it absolutely. Popper concedes that the Eccles–Popper theory of the soul does not meet this requirement. However, Eccles is quick to point out that the orthodox view that only the material is real is equally beyond disproof.

Eccles and Popper are not alone in their acceptance of certain metaphysical ideas. For example, in spite of the fact that MacKay calls himself a detractor of the Eccles–Popper theory, he holds a remarkably similar view about the mind–body problem. MacKay believes that the relationship between consciousness and the brain is the same as the relationship between a mathematical equation and a computer. Just as a nonphysical equation helps to determine the computer's behavior, MacKay believes a nonphysical self helps determine the physical brain's behavior—that the mind is the software of the brain. MacKay even harbors the hope that the "human equation" survives its host computer brain's death.

In a similar vein, the Caltech neurobiologist Roger Sperry, winner of the 1981 Nobel Prize for his work toward explaining the varying functions of the two hemispheres of the brain, asserts that consciousness is actually a newly emergent property of matter that appears only in such complex, hierarchically organized physical systems as the human brain. Sperry argues that consciousness as a whole thus somehow supersedes the combined functioning of the brain's 10 billion neurons. Sperry, however, is uncomfortable with the Eccles–Popper theory and accuses them of proposing the existence of supernatural agents. Eccles counters that it is only a matter of time before people like Sperry and MacKay realize they are believers in disguise. Such discussions about the ultimate nature of consciousness are not limited to the field of neurobiology. For the better part of a century, there has been a similar controversy in the field of physics. In the 1930s, John von Neumann turned his formidable intellect toward the puzzles of consciousness and reality emerging in quantum physics. This is especially noteworthy, for even among the most brilliant of his peers, von Neumann was considered a mind apart. Nobel Prize–winning physicist Hans Bethe once remarked, "I have sometimes wondered whether a brain like John von Neumann's does not indicate a species superior to that of man."[5]

Von Neumann's purpose in entering the subject of quantum physics was to wage a sort of cleanup campaign. However, after succeeding in bringing a much more rigorous mathematical understanding to quantum physics in general, he left, asserting the belief that the evidence suggested that man possesses a nonmatterial consciousness that can actually influence the world of matter. Von Neumann's mathematical understanding of quantum physics is still embedded firmly in current theory, but not surprisingly, many physicists are uneasy about his metaphysical conclusions.

Only a few call themselves believers. One of the most respected is Eugene Wigner, winner of the 1963 Nobel Prize in Physics and von Neumann's lifelong friend. Wigner believes that consciousness is not only an important concept to be considered in physics, but is, in a sense, the lathe of heaven. As Wigner sees it, the concept of objects existing apart from consciousness is meaningless. He feels that, in some strange way, consciousness actually enters in and helps create what is perceived as reality.[6] Needless to say, there are many scientists who do not hold Wigner's point of view. Karl Popper himself considers Wigner's arguments absurd and suggests instead that something is terribly wrong with von Neumann's approach.

Perhaps the most recent and exhaustive examination of the common ground between science and religion can be found in Paul Davies's 1983 book *God and the New Physics*. The central theme of the book explores what Davies calls "The Big Four questions of existence." These are:

1. Why are the laws of nature what they are?

2. Why does the Universe consist of the things it does?

3. How did these things arise?

4. How did the Universe achieve its organization?

Davies feels that such recent events as Guth's inflationary scenario and the Weinberg–Salam theory are beginning to provide tentative answers to these questions. According to Davies, modern physics has a significant bearing on many of the cosmological and metaphysical notions that underlie the entire history of religion. He feels that quantum theory does suggest that the mind–body problem is intimately connected with an accurate understanding of physics, and he is willing to consider the possibility that consciousness does exist as a program above and beyond the physical body—and, indeed, might survive physical death. However, he does not believe that these startling notions should provide the basis for any sort of religious system. As he states, "Science offers a surer path than religion in search of God."[7]

Davies is not without his critics. In a review of *God and the New Physics* in a July 1983 issue of *New Scientist*, David Bohm asserts that he is troubled that Davies feels science is so close to answering such basic cosmological and metaphysical questions as the Big Four. Bohm cautions that as recently as the late nineteenth century, a similar wave of "overconfidence" swept scientists when they felt that science was approaching at least the outlines of an absolute and final truth.

A second criticism that Bohm levels against Davies's conclusions is that the "answers" modern physics is developing lack clarity and, when pursued to their limits, aren't truly answers at all. The two major theoretical bedrocks of physics, relativity and quantum theory, don't even fit together coherently. Relativity implies to some that the whole of space–time is a single block, all laid out, and that our experience of time as a succession of flowing moments is illusory. Our sense of actually experiencing a present *now* is a purely subjective projection of "no real significance." Yet, quantum theory holds that physicists can only make statistical predictions about the phenomena that we will probably see at any moment, and says nothing at all about any kind of continuous substratum of existence that might underlie such "subjective" experiences.[8]

What about the biggest question of all: What does science currently say about God? Davies's use of the term *God* bothers Bohm most of all. Bohm is not disturbed by religion per se. What troubles him is Davies's notion that the essence of religion is necessarily a belief in some kind of God. Bohm points out that there are important religions, such as Buddhism and Vedanta, which are not based on belief in any kind of God.

But Bohm also takes his point further. As he states, "Some clue as to what may be the deeper essence of religion may be obtained by considering the derivation of the word; this is, according to the dictionary, either *re-ligere* or *relegare*. The first of these means 'to bind together,' and the second means 'to gather together.' This suggests that religion is most deeply concerned with man's impulse toward wholeness or integrity (as does also the word 'holy,' which means 'whole')."[9]

The wholeness that man seeks through religion suggests a problem to Bohm. In his view the institutional structure of both science and religion currently serve only to fragment our view of ourselves and the universe. As a solution, Bohm concludes that what humanity needs is a religious impulse toward wholeness that is open to "free rational scientific inquiry, in which no definable content is so sacred that it cannot be questioned."[10] Thus, Bohm is a physicist who disparages the notion of God but believes that a religious impulse is the surest path toward wholeness in science. And Davies is a physicist who disparages religion but believes that science is the surest path to an understanding of God.

What leads Davies to feel that God is a proper concept for consideration by a physicist? In *God and the New Physics,* he examines many of the more prominent arguments that have appeared throughout the history of religion and defrocks them one by one. For example, to the age-old notion that there must be a God because something had to have caused or created it all, Davies counters that physicists are familiar with the abrupt and uncaused appearance of particles in quantum physics and that Guth's inflationary scenario provides a natural explanation for the apparent abrupt appearance of the universe out of nothingness during the big bang. Similarly, to the argument that God must exist because such intricate and complex structures have arisen in the universe, Davies points out that there are many instances in physics and chemistry in which order and complex activity have arisen spontaneously.

However, there are certain intellectual territories in which Davies becomes less self-confident about denying the existence of

God. One of these is the uncanny way that mathematics has proved itself capable of describing the laws of nature. As Davies observes, "God is a mathematician" is an oft-repeated proclamation amongst scientists.

To Sidney Coleman, the notion that mathematics is "unreasonably" effective in describing the laws of nature is "a deep question." He states, "I don't know the answer to that. I oscillate. It could be that the development of physical thought has a more profound influence on the development of mathematics than we acknowledge. Certainly in the eighteenth and nineteenth centuries, mathematics was pushed by physics ideas. Then again in the modern era, of course, mathematics is much more autonomous, mathematicians listen much more to themselves than they listen to anyone else. They develop mathematics in its own direction. In this regard, in the twentieth century they've developed a stupendous amount of mathematics, only a tiny fraction of which turns out to be applicable in physics. So maybe out of this huge world of mathematics we have picked the theories that have proven effective in describing phenomena."[11]

Davies sees more profound evidence of God in the findings of the new physics. The fact that there are laws of physics at all is nothing short of miraculous. Such laws or regularities in nature are not logically necessary: "We can envisage a capricious world, full of random processes and haphazard concatenations of events, a world where matter and energy go berserk."[12]

But as Davies sees it, even more importantly, such laws are themselves based on an incredible string of improbable accidents or coincidences. These coincidences felicitously result in the "constants of nature," and were it not for this host of improbable accidents, the universe would not be able to exist at all. Such constants of nature include the masses of the elementary particles, the strengths of the couplings between different fields of matter, and so on. For example, as Davies points out, if the strong nuclear force holding together the nuclei of atoms were just a fraction weaker than it is, atomic nuclei would become unstable and disintegrate. It would then be impossible for even the simplest of elements, such as deuterium (heavy hydrogen), to exist. Because deuterium is a necessary link in the chain of nuclear reactions that fuel the stars, they would in turn stop shining. If the strong nuclear force were just slightly more powerful, it would be possible for two protons to overcome their mutual electric repulsion and stick together. If this had occurred during the big bang, it would have been impossible for hydrogen to form; again, no stars such as the Sun would be able to exist, nor could liquid water. Life as we know it would not have been able to form.

Similarly, if the gravitational constant were only slightly different, the universe as we know it would not have been able to form. If the strengths of the gravitational forces were altered by a mere one part in $10^{40}$, such stars as the Sun would not be able to exist, and so on, and so on. Davies concludes, "The seemingly miraculous occurence of numerical values that nature has assigned to her fundamental constants must remain the most compelling evidence for an element of cosmic design. . . . It is hard to resist the impression that the present structure of the universe, apparently so sensitive to minor alterations in the numbers, has been rather carefully thought out. Such a conclusion can, of course, only be subjective. In the end it boils down to a question of belief." [13]

# Epilogue: *The Reality Club*

The Reality Club is an informal association I organized during the 1970s to explore the idea that the most interesting way to arrive at the edge of the world's knowledge is to seek out the most complex and sophisticated minds, put them in a room together, and have them ask each other the questions they are asking themselves. Over the years, in New York and San Francisco, in hotel rooms, Chinese restaurants, university classrooms, and private homes, I have invited numerous speakers to present their work and ideas to a peer group in free-for-all meetings, with the understanding that they will be challenged. Membership is limited to people who, through their work and ideas, have reinvented the universe. Many of the people quoted in this book have presented their work to The Reality Club. Others include psychologist Rollo May, feminist Betty Friedan, religious historians Elaine Pagels and Gilles Quispel, and anthropologists Michael Harner and Mary Catherine Bateson.

At Reality Club meetings, we often end up in vigorous, impolite arguments. This level of debate, the intensity with which we advance our ideas to each other, strikes me as not inconsistent with the way in which we invent the universe. All of us have in our minds an image of a universe of unimaginable vastness preceded in linear fashion by eons in time. But is that the way it really is? Is the universe *there* at all? Is it an a priori entity existing in space, in time, with a past and a future, something to be discovered, decoded, its mysteries unraveled? Or is it the scientists themselves simply looking into their own heads, creating their own construct out of words and tools?

My own point of view, one that I have advanced perhaps too frequently to my Reality Club colleagues, is that we create the world and that the universe is a creation of our language, our perceptions. Within The Reality Club this has led over the years to interesting discussions and running arguments with several of the eminent scientist members. At one particular meeting, which was held at the Cohen Library of Rockefeller University, two molecular biologists were in a dispute concerning evolutionary developments that, according to one, occurred some billions of years ago. While I could not take issue with the scientific evidence for such developments, I had to ask how anyone could know anything about what happened billions of years ago. Indeed, what does "a billion years" mean?

At another meeting, a physicist, holding forth at the Council Room of the New York Academy of the Sciences, was explaining some of the recent theories concerning the first moments of the universe's creation. Just ten years ago we would have been content to talk about "the first three minutes." His talk concerned what happened at $10^{-45}$ seconds. I began to question the meaningfulness of talking about an infinitesimal fraction of a second in the creation of the universe. What does it mean to talk about the universe's having a beginning at all? Are we really just talking about tools of our own making, including the words we use to describe our universe? Indeed, every few years science comes up with a new telescope, a new tool, and the universe becomes magnitudes larger or more complex.

I recall traveling to California in 1974 to meet with Gregory Bateson. He had recently proposed writing a book, entitled *The Evolutionary Idea,* in which he was going to challenge the most recent conventional wisdom among evolutionists. Bateson's premise was that Darwin's survival-of-the-fittest theories applied to ideas about evolution rather than to organic evolutionary processes themselves. Although he readily admitted there was a reality outside our heads, he still believed we created the world through our perceptions of it. I have a vivid memory of standing in a moonlit parking lot in Malibu. Bateson was backing away from the book. He could not, he would not write it. "Why?" I inquired. "Because," he responded, "evolutionists kill each other." He recounted a story about his father, William Bateson, a geneticist and a preeminent member of the British scientific establishment at the turn of the century. Bateson's father had taken issue with experiments conducted by Austrian biologist William Kammerer concerning suggested inherited characteristics of the midwife toad. Had Kammerer's findings prevailed, evolutionary theories set forth by Lamarck would have gained support. As it happened, William Bateson, a Darwinist, was able to show that experimental results were unreliable. Kammerer's work was discredited. He committed suicide. Lamarckism became a dead issue.

Bateson told the story to make the point that we do not live in some kind of idealized objective universe, but in a construct of human ideas constantly shifting and subject to revision, to repudiation. At this late stage in his life and his career, he was increasingly more sympathetic to a Lamarckian position, a point of view that would put him in direct opposition to the major evolutionists of his own day. At the age of seventy-one, suffering from a variety of physical ailments, he was not up to the fight. Debate among scientists is often debate over which invention, which construct will win out. Several years later, his book, ultimately written under the title *Mind and Nature,* avoided a major confrontation on this issue.

Sometimes I ask myself, "Who's crazy?" Scientists stand at the edge of the darkness and see unimaginable depths, vastnesses, magnitudes, the infinite. I stand at the same spot. I see people, language, ideas, intellectual desire. "Who's crazy?" One night at a scientific dinner I had the good fortune to sit next to one of the world's more vocal and articulate physicists. During the meal he grumbled on about jogging as evidence of the decline of Western civilization. "They don't understand what's important. Only the spiritual matters," he said. "Einstein never had to exercise," he exclaimed. "These people"—referring to the joggers running past his window every day—"are materialists. They don't understand the beauty, the almost spiritual quality of the physical. It's all in the mind. It's not material. It's a mental phenomenon."

The conversation drifted into ideas about the nature of scientific discovery. "What universe?" I asked at one point, responding to what I presumed to be his thoughts on the mental aspect of the physical. "Don't worry about it," he said, "the universe is there. That's what science is all about. I can create experiments that allow me to make certain successful predictions," he went on. "Other scientists in another place and at another time can then successfully duplicate the experiments and achieve the same results. Thus, science works."

Who am I to argue the success of the scientific method with a Nobel laureate? Yes, science works. And with it we get the benefits of modern technology and medicine, the uncertainties of biotechnology and genetic engineering, and the reality of the possibility of self-destruction. Science works. But can the scientist appreciate that we create the world we perceive, that the data we collect, the experiments we conduct all lead ultimately to self-referential models? Perhaps this is what Wallace Stevens had in mind when he wrote of poetry that it "has to be more than a conception of the world. It has to be a revelation of nature. Conceptions are artificial. Perceptions are essential." [1]

We do not discover the universe, we invent it, and reinvent it. We, its observers, are part of that invention and made out of the same stuff. If we are to talk about the universe as existing apart from us, we must say that the universe is constructed so as to be able to observe itself. In the end, the universe, being everything, is not comparable to anything else. It simply is. I like to think of it as "The Reality Club."

# NOTES

# BIBLIOGRAPHY

# Notes

## INTRODUCTION

1. Stevens, Wallace, "Adagia," *Opus Posthumous* (New York: Alfred A. Knopf, 1975), p. 163.
2. Ibid., p. 164.

## INTRODUCTION TO PART I: THE COSMOLOGICAL UNIVERSE

1. Pais, Abraham, *"Subtle Is the Lord . . .": The Science and Life of Albert Einstein* (New York: Oxford University Press, 1982).
2. Ibid.

### The Inflationary Scenario

1. Jastrow, Robert, *God and the Astronomers* (New York: Warner Books, 1978).
2. Guth, Alan H., and Steinhardt, Paul J., "The Inflationary Universe." Unpublished paper dated August 18, 1983.
3. Conversation with Guth, August 22, 1983.
4. Ibid.
5. Overbye, Dennis, "The Universe According to Guth," *Discover* (June 1983).
6. Ibid.
7. Davies, Paul, *God and the New Physics* (London: J. M. Dent & Sons, 1983).

8. Ibid.
9. Conversation with Guth, August 22, 1983.

*A Hole in the Universe*

1. Waldrop, M. Mitchell, "The Large-Scale Structure of the Universe," *Science* 219 (March 1983).
2. Waldrop, M. Mitchell, "Delving the Hole in Space," *Science* 214 (November 1981).
3. Zeldovich, Ya. B., Einasto, J., Shandarin, S. F., "Giant Voids in the Universe," *Nature* 300 (December 1982).
4. Waldrop, "Delving the Hole in Space."

*Ninety-seven Percent of the Universe Is Missing*

1. Silk, Joseph, "The Missing Mass—Now It's a Gravitino! *Nature* 297 (May 1982).
2. Gott, J. R., III, Schramm, D. N., Gunn, J. E., Tinsley, B. M., "An Unbound Universe?" *Astrophysics Journal* 194 (1974).
3. Rubin, Vera C., "The Rotation of Spiral Galaxies," *Science* 220 (June 1983).
4. Editors, "Neutrinos—A Case of Mistaken Identity?" *New Scientist* (24 June 1981).
5. Waldrop, Mitchell M., "Neutrinos: No Oscillations?" *Science* 216 (May 1982).
6. Primack, Joel, and Pagels, Heinz, "Supersymmetry, Cosmology and New Physics at Terraelectronvolt Energies," *Physical Review Letters* 48, no. 4 (January 1982).
7. Waldrop, M. Mitchell, "More Than a Planet, Almost a Star," *Science* 227 (4 January 1985).
8. Gribbin, John, "The Fate of the Universe," *New Scientist* (27 November 1980).
9. Ibid.
10. Dicus, Duane, et al., "The Future of the Universe," *Scientific American* (January 1982).
11. Ibid.
12. Stevens, Wallace, "Final Soliloquy of the Interior Paramour," *The Collected Poems of Wallace Stevens* (New York: Alfred A. Knopf, 1967).

### The Case of the Incredible Shrinking Sun

1. Eddy, Jack, and Boornazian, A. A., "Secular Decrease in the Solar Diameter 1863–1953," *American Astronomical Society Bulletin* 11, no. 437 (1979).
2. Shapiro, Irwin, "Is the Sun Shrinking?" *Science* 208 (1980).
3. Dunham, D., Fiala, A., Herald, D., Muller, P., and Sofia, S., "Observation of a Probable Change in the Solar Radius Between 1715 and 1979, *Science* 210 (1980).
4. Gribbin, John, "The Curious Case of the Shrinking Sun," *New Scientist* (3 March 1983).

### Something Strange at the Center of the Milky Way

1. Waldrop, M. Mitchell, "A Hole in the Milky Way," *Science* (June 1979).
2. Ibid.
3. Ibid.
4. Lynden-Bell, D., *Nuclei of Galaxies,* ed. D.J.K. O'Connell, S.J., *Vatican* (April 1970).
5. Townes, C. H., Lacy, J. H., Geballe, T. R., and Hollenbach, D. J., "The Centre of the Galaxy," *Nature* 301 (February 1983).

### Mining Energy from a Black Hole

1. Wheeler, John, Misner, Charles, and Thorne, Kip, *Gravitation* (San Francisco: W. H. Freeman, 1973).
2. Chapline, George F., "Cosmologial Effects of Primordial Black Holes," *Nature* (1975).
3. Bekenstein, J., "Black Holes and Entropy," *Physical Review* D7 (1973).
4. Davies, Paul, "On Being Lowered into a Black Hole," *New Scientist* (14 January 1982).
5. Ibid.

### The .001557806449023-Second Pulsar

1. Helfand, David J., "A Superfast New Pulsar," *Nature* 300 (December 1982).
2. Waldrop, M. Mitchell, "The 0.001557806449023-Second Pulsar," *Science* 219 (February 1983).

## *The Age of the Universe Crisis*

1. "'Age of Universe' Crisis Worsens," *New Scientist* (23 September 1982).
2. Ibid.
3. Ibid.
4. Ibid.
5. Van den Bergh, Sidney, "Size and Age of the Universe," *Science* 213 (August 1981).

## PART II: THE QUANTUM UNIVERSE

## *Introduction*

1. Davies, Paul, *Superforce* (New York: Simon & Schuster, 1984).

## *Quantum Theory Comes of Age*

1. Empson, William, "Doctrinal Point," in *Collected Poems* (New York: Harcourt, Brace & Co., 1949).
2. Clauser, John, and Freedman, Stuart, "Experimental Test of Local Hidden Variable Theories," *Physical Review Letters* 28 (1972).
3. Aspect, A., Grangier, P., Roger, G., *Physical Review Letters* 49, no. 91 (1982).
4. Rohrlich, Fritz, "Facing Quantum Mechanical Reality," *Science* 221 (September 1983).
5. Bohm, David, *Wholeness and the Implicate Order* (London: Routledge & Kegan Paul, 1980).
6. Pagels, Heinz, *The Cosmic Code* (New York: Simon & Schuster, 1982).

## *Broken Symmetries and Grand Unified Fields*

1. Coleman, Sidney, "The 1979 Nobel Prize in Physics," *Science* 206 (December 1979).
2. Ibid.
3. Ibid.
4. Weinberg, Steven, "Conceptual Foundations of the Unified Theory of Weak and Electromagnetic Interactions," *Science* 210 (December 1980).
5. Ibid.

6. Coleman, "The 1979 Nobel Prize."
7. Weinberg, Steven, *The First Three Minutes* (New York: Basic Books, 1977).
8. Ibid.
9. Ibid.
10. Davies, Paul, *Superforce* (New York: Simon & Schuster, 1984).
11. Bateson, *Steps to an Ecology of Mind* (New York: Ballantine, 1972).

### *The Capture of the Elusive W*

1. Gold, Michael, "Chasing Particles of Unity," *Science 83* (March 1983).
2. Sutton, Christine, "The Quest for the W Particle," *New Scientist* (27 January 1983).
3. Gold, "Chasing Particles."

### *Quarks and Demon Nuclei*

1. Pagels, *The Cosmic Code.*
2. Robinson, Arthur L., "Cornell Evidence for Fifth Quark," *Science* 209 (September 1980).
3. Pagels, *The Cosmic Code.*
4. Friedlander, E. M., et al., *Physical Review Letters* 45, no. 1084 (1980).
5. Fredriksson, S., and Jandl, M., *Physical Review Letters* 48, no. 14 (1982).
6. Lipkin, H. J., *WIS Report* 82, no. 2 (January 1982).
7. Stein, Gertrude, *Lectures in America* (Boston: Beacon Press, 1935).

## PART III: THE BIOLOGICAL UNIVERSE

### *The Death of the Dinosaurs*

1. Alvarez, W., Alvarez, L. W., Asaro, F., & Michel, H. V., *Geological Society of America, Abstracts with Program* 11, no. 350 (1979).
2. Smit, J., and Hertogen, J., *Nature* 285 (1980).
3. Ibid.
4. Ganapathy, R., *Science* 209 (1980).
5. Kyte, F., Zhou, Z., and Wasson, J. T., *Nature* 288 (1980).
6. Hsu, Kenneth, *Nature* 285.
7. Kyte, Zhou, and Wasson, *op. cit.*

8. Alvarez, L., Alvarez, W., Asaro, F., Michel, H., "Extraterrestrial Cause for Cretaceous–Tertiary Extinction," *Science* 208 (6 June 1980).
9. Klaver, G., *Nature* 292 (1981).
10. Allaby, Michael, and Lovelock, James, *The Great Extinction* (Garden City, NY: Doubleday and Company, 1983).
11. Allaby and Lovelock, *The Great Extinction.*
12. Kerr, Richard A., "Asteroid Theory of Extinctions Strengthened," *Science* 210 (31 October 1980).
13. Ibid.
14. Ibid.
15. Whipple, Fred, *New Scientist* 89, no. 1245 (1981).
16. Alvarez, L., Alvarez, W., Asaro, F., and Michel, H., "Extraterrestrial Cause."
17. Raup, D., and Sepkoski, J., *Proceedings of the National Academy of Sciences* 81 (1982).
18. Rampino, M., and Stothers, R., "Terrestrial Mass Extinctions, Cometary Impacts and the Sun's Motion Perpendicular to the Galactic Plane," *Nature* 308 (April 1984).
19. Schwartz, R., and James, P., "Periodic Mass Extinctions and the Sun's Oscillation about the Galactic Plane," *Nature* 308 (April 1984).
20. Whitmire, D., and Jackson, A., "Are Periodic Mass Extinctions Driven by a Distant Solar Companion?" *Nature* 308 (April 1984).
21. Angier, Natalie, "Did Comets Kill the Dinosaurs?" *Time* (6 May 1985).

## Is Darwin Evolving?

1. Lewin, Roger, "Evolutionary Theory under Fire," *Science* 210 (November 1980).
2. Ibid.
3. Charlesworth, Brian, "Neo-Darwinism—The Plain Truth," *New Scientist* (15 April 1982).
4. Lewin, Roger, "Do Jumping Genes Make Evolutionary Leaps?" *Science* 213 (7 August 1981).
5. Ibid.
6. Ibid.
7. Ibid.

8. Ibid.
9. Ibid.
10. Vines, Gail, "Molecular Drive: A Third Force in Evolution," *New Scientist* (9 December 1982).
11. Lewin, Roger, "Jumping Genes."
12. Lewin, Roger, "Evolutionary Theory under Fire."
13. Dawkins, Richard, *The Selfish Gene* (London: Oxford University Press, 1976).

## Sociobiology and the Selfish Gene

1. Wilson, Edward O., *Sociobiology: The New Synthesis* (Cambridge, MA: Harvard University Press, 1975).
2. Ibid.
3. Ibid.
4. Ibid.
5. Ibid.
6. Ibid.
7. Lumsden, Charles J., and Wilson, Edward O., *Genes, Mind, and Culture: The Coevolutionary Process* (Boston: Harvard University Press, 1981).
8. Batten, Mary, "Why Men Rape," *Science Digest* 90, no. 7 (July 1982).
9. Ibid.
10. Dawkins, Richard, *The Selfish Gene.*
11. Lewontin, Richard C., "Sleight of Hand," *The Sciences* (July/August 1981).
12. Ibid.
13. Gould, Stephen Jay, "Genes on the Brain," *The New York Review of Books* (April 1982).
14. Ibid.
15. Saver, Jeffrey, "Edward O. Wilson: Father of a New Science," *Science Digest* 90, no. 5 (May 1982).

## Symbiosis and Cell Evolution

1. Margulis, Lynn, *Symbiosis and Cell Evolution* (San Francisco: W. H. Freeman, 1981).
2. Margulis, Lynn, and Sagan, Dorion, *The Expanding Microcosm: Four Billion Years of Evolution.* Work in progress.

3. Harrar, George, "Microcosmos," *The Boston Globe Magazine* (11 September 1983).
4. Nagel, Ernest, "Relativity and Twentieth Century Intellectual Life," in Woolf, Harry, ed., *Some Strangeness in the Proportion* (Reading, MA: Addison Wesley, 1980).

### When Man Stopped Being an Ape

1. Nuttall, George H. F., *Blood Immunity and Blood Relationships* (New York: Macmillan, 1904).
2. Goodman, Morris, "Evolution of the Immunologic Species Specificity of Human Serum Proteins," *Human Biology* 34 (1962).
3. Cherfas, Jeremy, and Gribbin, John, "The Molecular Making of Mankind," *New Scientist* (27 August 1981).
4. Sarich, Vincent, and Wilson, Allan, "An Immunological Timescale for Hominid Evolution," *Science* 158 (1967).
5. Cherfas and Gribbin, "The Molecular Making of Mankind."
6. Gribbin, John, and Cherfas, Jeremy, *The Monkey Puzzle: Reshaping the Evolutionary Tree* (New York: Pantheon, 1982).
7. Ibid.
8. Dubos, René, *Celebration of Life* (New York: McGraw-Hill, 1981).

### Lamarck Lives

1. Lewin, Roger, "Lamarck Will Not Lie Down," *Science* 213 (July 1982).
2. Ibid.
3. Medawar, Sir Peter, "New Evolutionary Mechanism?" *The New York Times* (22 March 1981).
4. Lewin, "Lamarck Will Not Lie Down."
5. Medawar, "New Evolutionary Mechanism?"

### Genetic Engineering

1. McAuliffe, Kathleen, and McAuliffe, Sharon, "Keeping Up with the Genetic Revolution," *The New York Times Magazine* (6 November 1983).
2. Sutton, Christine, "Genetic Engineers Sweep the Board," *New Scientist* (23 October 1980).

3. Golden, Frederic, "Shaping Life in the Lab," *Time* (9 March 1981).
4. Ibid.
5. McAuliffe, Kathleen, and McAuliffe, Sharon, "The Genetic Assault on Cancer," *The New York Times Magazine* (24 October 1982).
6. Ibid.
7. DeMott, John S., "Test-Tube Life: Reg. U.S. Pat. Off.," *Time* (30 June 1980).
8. Wade, Nicholas, "Gene Splicing Company Wows Wall Street," *Science* 210 (October 1980).
9. DeMott, "Test-Tube Life."
10. Ibid.
11. McAuliffe, Kathleen, and McAuliffe, Sharon, "Keeping Up with the Genetic Revolution."
12. Ibid.
13. Ibid.

## Maximum Life Span

1. Hart, R., and Setlow, R., "Correlation between Deoxyribonucleic Acid Excision Repair and Lifespan in a Number of Mammalian Species," *Proceedings, National Academy of Sciences* 71, no. 2169 (1974).
2. Tas, S., Tam, C. F., and Walford, R. L., "Disulfide Bonds and the Structure of the Chromatin Complex in Relation to Aging," *Mechanisms of Aging and Development* 12, no. 65 (1980).
3. Walford, Roy L., *Maximum Life Span* (New York: W. W. Norton, 1983).
4. Ibid.
5. Ibid.
6. Ibid.
7. Ibid.
8. Ibid.
9. Editors, "Move Over Methusaleh! (Or P. T. Barnum?)," *Harvard Medical School Health Letter* (November 1983).
10. Walford, Roy L., "The Extension of Maximum Life Span," *Geriatric Clinics of North America* 1 (in press 1985).
11. Walford, *Maximum Life Span.*

## *The Oncogene*

1. Weinberg, Robert A., "A Molecular Basis of Cancer," *Scientific American* 249, no. 5 (November 1983).
2. McAuliffe, Kathleen, and McAuliffe, Sharon, "The Genetic Assault on Cancer."
3. Weinberg, "A Molecular Basis of Cancer."
4. Ibid.
5. Ibid.
6. McAuliffe and McAuliffe, "The Genetic Assault on Cancer."
7. Weinberg, "A Molecular Basis of Cancer."
8. Ibid.
9. Logan, Jonathan, and Cairns, John, "The Secret of Cancer," *Nature* 300 (11 November 1982).

## *What Is Life?*

1. Lovelock, James, *Gaia: A New Look at Life on Earth* (New York: Oxford University Press, 1979).
2. Eiseley, Loren.
3. Feinberg, Gerald, and Shapiro, Robert, *Life Beyond Earth: The Intelligent Earthling's Guide to Life in the Universe* (New York: William Morrow, 1980).
4. Ibid.
5. Stevens, Wallace, "Man Made Out of Words," in Stevens, *Collected Poems*.

## PART IV: THE MATHEMATICAL UNIVERSE

## *Introduction*

1. Wiener, Norbert, *The Human Use of Human Beings: Cybernetics and Society* (New York: Avon, 1967).

## *Fractals*

1. Mandlebrot, Benoit B., *Fractals: Form, Chance and Dimension* (San Francisco: W. H. Freeman and Company, 1977).
2. Ibid.

## Catastrophe Theory

1. Thompson, D'Arcy, *On Growth and Form* (Cambridge, England: Cambridge University Press, 1942).
2. Ibid.
3. Thom, René, *Structural Stability and Morphogenesis* (Reading, MA: Addison Wesley, 1975).
4. Ibid.
5. Feinberg, Gerald, *Solid Clues* (New York: Simon & Schuster, 1985).
6. Thom, *Structural Stability.*
7. Sheldrake, Rupert, *A New Science of Life* (Los Angeles: J. P. Tarcher, 1981).
8. Feinberg, *Solid Clues.*

## Chaos and Strange Attractors

1. Gleick, James, "Solving the Mathematical Riddle of Chaos," *The New York Times Magazine* (10 June 1984).
2. Peterson, Ivars, "Pathways to Chaos," *Science News* 124 (30 July 1983).
3. Peterson, Ivars, "Jupiter's Spot of Order in Chaos," *Science News* 125 (2 June 1984).
4. Reiter, Carla, "The Turbulent Nature of a Chaotic World," *New Scientist* (31 May 1984).
5. Ibid.

## Cellular Automata

1. Wolfman, Stephen, "University and Complexity in Cellular Automata," *Physica 10D* (New York: Elsevier Science Publishers, 1984).
2. Hayes, Brian, "Computer Recreations," *Scientific American* (March 1984).
3. Wright, Robert, "The Information Age," *The Sciences* (January/February 1985).
4. Hillis, W. Daniel, "The Connection Machine: A Computer Architecture Based on Cellular Automata," *Physica 10D* (New York: Elsevier Science Publishers, 1984).

## The Fifth Generation of Computers

1. Dreyfus, Hubert L., *What Computers Can't Do* (New York: Harper & Row, 1979).
2. Waldrop, M. Mitchell, "Artificial Intelligence (I): Into the World," *Science* 223 (February 1984).
3. Kolata, Gina, "How Can Computers Get Common Sense?" *Science* 217 (September 1982).
4. Ibid.
5. Bateson, Gregory, *Mind and Nature* (New York: E. P. Dutton, 1979).
6. Kolata, "How Can Computers Get Common Sense?"
7. Ibid.
8. Waldrop, "Artificial Intelligence (I)."
9. Dreyfus, *What Computers Can't Do.*
10. Herman, Rox, "Computing with a Human Face," *New Scientist* (6 May 1982).
11. Dreyfus, *What Computers Can't Do.*
12. Feigenbaum, Edward A., and McCorduck, Pamela, *The Fifth Generation: Japan's Computer Challenge to the World* (Reading, MA: Addison Wesley, 1983).

## Massive Parallelism

1. Waldrop, M. Mitchell, "Artificial Intelligence in Parallel," *Science* (August 1984).
2. Solomon, Stephen, "Superbrain: The Race to Create the World's Fastest Computer," *Science Digest* (September 1983).
3. "It's Like Being at Kitty Hawk," *Business Week* (9 July 1984).
4. Waldrop, "Artificial Intelligence."

## PART V: THE UNORTHODOX UNIVERSE

### Wholeness and the Implicate Order

1. Temple, Robert, "David Bohm," *New Scientist,* 11 November 1982.
2. Bohm, David, *Wholeness and the Implicate Order* (London: Routledge & Kegan Paul, 1980).
3. Temple, "David Bohm."
4. Ibid.

5. Bohm, *Wholeness and the Implicate Order.*
6. Weber, Renee, "Nature as Creativity," *ReVision* 5, no. 2 (Fall 1982).
7. Bohm, *Wholeness and the Implicate Order.*
8. Temple, "David Bohm."
9. Brown, G. Spencer, *Laws of Form.*

### Did Man Really Fall to Earth?

1. Margulis, Lynn, *Early Life* (Boston: Science Books International, 1982).
2. Hoyle, F., and Wickramasinghe, N. C., "Does Epidemic Disease Come from Space?" *New Scientist* 76 (1977).
3. Wickramasinghe, N. C., "Where Life Begins," *New Scientist* 74 (1977).
4. Temperley, H. N. V., "Could Life Have Happened by Accident?" *New Scientist* (19 August 1982).
5. Shapiro, Robert, *Origins: How Life Began on Earth.* Work in progress.

### Morphogenetic Fields

1. Sheldrake, Rupert, *A New Science of Life* (London: Blond & Briggs, 1981).
2. Ibid.
3. Driesch, H., *Science and Philosophy of the Organism* (London: A. & C. Black, 1980).
4. Sheldrake, *A New Science of Life.*
5. Ibid.
6. Ibid.
7. Lewis, Peter, "Are We All on the Same Wavelength?" *The Times* (London) (6 May 1983).
8. Editors, *Nature* 301 (24 February 1983).
9. Conversation with Sheldrake, February 1983.
10. Holden, A., and Singer, P., *Crystals and Crystal Growing* (London: Heinemann, 1961).
11. Conversation with Sheldrake, February 1983.
12. Sheldrake, R., and Weber, R., "Morphogenetic Fields: Nature's Habits?" *ReVision* 5, no. 2 (Fall 1982).
13. Bohm, David, *Wholeness and the Implicate Order.*

14. Bohm, D., and Weber, R., "Nature as Creativity," *ReVision* 5, no. 2 (Fall 1982).
15. Sheldrake, R., and Bohm, D., "Morphogenetic Fields and the Implicate Order," *ReVision* 5, no. 2 (Fall 1982).
16. "Turkish Nursery Rhyme to Test Theory," *New Scientist* (April 1983).

### Science, God, and the Soul

1. Gliedman, John, "Scientists in Search of a Soul," *Science Digest* 90, (July 1982).
2. Eccles, Sir John, and Robinson, Daniel N., *The Wonder of Being Human* (New York: The Free Press, 1984).
3. Miller, George A., "When We Think, What Thinks?" *The New York Times Book Review* (26 August 1984).
4. Gliedman, "Scientists in Search of a Soul."
5. Heims, Steve J., *John von Neumann and Norbert Wiener* (Cambridge, MA: MIT Press, 1982).
6. Wigner, Eugene, *Symmetries and Reflections* (Bloomington: Indiana University Press, 1967).
7. Davies, Paul, *God and the New Physics* (London: J. M. Dent & Sons, 1983).
8. Bohm, David, "Can Science Save the Fragmenting Universe?" *New Scientist* (July 1983).
9. Ibid.
10. Ibid.
11. Conversation with Sydney Coleman (31 January 1983).
12. Davies, Paul, "God and the New Physics," *New Scientist* (June 1983).
13. Ibid.

### Epilogue

1. Stevens, Wallace, "Adagia," p. 162.

# Bibliography

Allaby, Michael, and Lovelock, James. *The Great Extinction.* Garden City, NY: Doubleday, 1983.

Bateson, Gregory. *Mind and Nature.* New York: E. P. Dutton, 1979.

————. *Steps to an Ecology of Mind.* New York: Ballantine Books, 1972.

Beckett, Samuel. *Three Novels.* New York: Grove Press, 1955.

Bell, E. T. *Men of Mathematics.* New York: Simon & Schuster, 1965.

Berman, Morris. *The Reenchantment of the World.* Ithaca, NY: Cornell University Press, 1981.

Bernstein, Jeremy. *The Analytical Engine.* New York: William Morrow, 1981.

————. *Experiencing Science.* New York: E. P. Dutton, 1978.

————. *Science Observed.* New York: Basic Books, 1982.

Bohm, David. *Wholeness and the Implicate Order.* London: Routledge & Kegan Paul, 1980.

Bohr, Niels. *Atomic Physics and Human Knowledge.* New York: Science Editions, 1961.

————. *Essays 1958–1962 on Atomic Physics and Human Knowledge.* New York: Vintage Books, 1966.

Born, Max. *The Born–Einstein Letters.* New York: Walker and Company, 1971.

Brillouin, Leon. *Science and Information Theory.* New York: Academic Press, 1962.

————. *Scientific Uncertainty and Information.* New York: Academic Press, 1964.

Brinnin, John Malcolm. *The Third Rose: Gertrude Stein and Her World.* Boston: Little, Brown and Company, 1959.

Brockman, John. *Afterwords.* Garden City, NJ: Anchor Press, 1973.

———. *By the Late John Brockman*. New York: Macmillan, 1970.

———. *37*. New York: Holt, Rinehart & Winston, 1970.

Bronowski, Jacob. *The Origins of Knowledge and Imagination*. New Haven, CT: Yale University Press, 1978.

Brown, G. Spencer. *Laws of Form*. New York: E. P. Dutton, 1972.

Burnham, Jack. *Beyond Modern Sculpture*. New York: George Braziller, 1968.

Calder, Nigel. *Einstein's Universe*. New York: Viking Press, 1979.

———. *The Key to the Universe*. New York: Viking Press, 1977.

Calvin, William. *The Throwing Madonna*. New York: McGraw-Hill, 1983.

Campbell, Jeremy. *Grammatical Man*. New York: Simon & Schuster, 1982.

Chaisson, Eric. *Cosmic Dawn*. Boston: Atlantic Monthly Press, 1981.

Chargoff, Erwin. *Heraclitian Fire*. New York: Warner Books, 1980.

Clark, Ronald W. *Einstein: The Life and Times*. New York: World Publishing, 1971.

Cloud, Preston. *Cosmos, Earth and Man*. New Haven, CT: Yale University Press, 1978.

Crick, Francis. *Life Itself: Its Origins and Nature*. New York: Simon & Schuster, 1981.

Davies, Paul. *The Accidental Universe*. Cambridge, England: Cambridge University Press, 1982.

———. *The Edge of Infinity*. New York: Simon & Schuster, 1981.

———. *God and the New Physics*. London: J. M. Dent & Sons, 1983.

———. *Other Worlds*. New York: Simon & Schuster, 1980.

———. *The Runaway Universe*. New York: Harper & Row, 1981.

———. *Superforce*. New York: Simon & Schuster, 1984.

Davis, Philip, and Hersh, Reuben. *The Mathematical Experience*. Boston: Houghton Mifflin, 1981.

Dawkins, Richard. *The Selfish Gene*. London: Oxford University Press, 1976.

Dennett, Daniel C. *Brainstorms*. Cambridge, MA: MIT Press, 1978.

Dreyfus, Hubert C. *What Computers Can't Do*. New York: Harper & Row, 1972, 1979.

Dubos, René. *Celebration of Life*. New York: McGraw-Hill, 1981.

———. *Man Adapting*. New Haven, CT: Yale University Press, 1967.

Dyson, Freeman. *Disturbing the Universe*. New York: Harper & Row, 1979.

Eccles, Sir John, and Robinson, Daniel N. *The Wonder of Being Human*. New York: The Free Press, 1984.

Eigen, Manfred, and Winkler, Ruthild. *Laws of the Game*. New York: Alfred A. Knopf, 1981.

Einstein, Albert. *The Evolution of Physics*. With Leopold Infeld. New York: Simon & Schuster, 1938.

————. *Ideas and Opinions*. Translated by Sonja Bergmann. New York: Crown Publishers, 1954.

————. *The Meaning of Relativity*. Princeton, NJ: Princeton University Press.

————. *Out of My Later Years*. New York: Philosophical Library, 1950.

————. *Relativity*. New York: Crown Publishers, 1961.

————. *The World as I See It*. New York: Philosophical Library, 1949.

Eliot, T. S. *The Complete Poems and Plays, 1909–1950*. New York: Harcourt, Brace & World, 1962.

Empson, William. *Collected Poems*. New York: Harcourt Brace and Company, 1949.

Feigenbaum, Edward A., and McCorduck, Pamela. *The Fifth Generation: Japan's Computer Challenge to the World*. Reading, MA: Addison-Wesley, 1983.

Feinberg, Gerald. *Solid Clues*. New York: Simon & Schuster, 1985.

————. *What Is the World Made Of?* Garden City, NY: Anchor Press, 1978.

————, and Shapiro, Robert. *Life Beyond Earth: The Intelligent Earthling's Guide to Life in the Universe*. New York: William Morrow, 1982.

Ferris, Tim. *Galaxies*. San Francisco: Sierra Club Books, 1980.

————. *The Red Limit*. New York: William Morrow, 1982.

French, A. P., editor. *Einstein: A Centenary Volume*. Cambridge, MA: Harvard University Press, 1979.

Gamow, George. *One Two Three . . . Infinity: Facts and Speculations of Science*. New York: Viking Press, 1947.

Goldstein, Thomas. *The Dawn of Modern Science*. Boston: Houghton Mifflin, 1980.

Goldstine, Herman H. *The Computer from Pascal to von Neumann*. Princeton, NJ: Princeton University Press, 1972.

Gould, Stephen Jay. *The Mismeasure of Man.* New York: W. W. Norton, 1981.

———. *The Panda's Thumb: More Reflections in Natural History.* New York: W. W. Norton, 1980.

Gregory, Richard L. *Mind in Science.* Cambridge, England: Cambridge University Press, 1981.

Gribbin, John, and Cherfas, Jeremy. *The Monkey Puzzle: Reshaping the Evolutionary Tree.* New York: Pantheon Books, 1982.

Harwit, Martin. *Cosmic Discovery.* New York: Basic Books, 1981.

Haugeland, John. *Mind Design.* Cambridge, MA: MIT Press, 1981.

Heims, Steve J. *John von Neumann and Norbert Wiener.* Cambridge, MA: MIT Press, 1981.

Heisenberg, Werner. *Philosophic Problems of Nuclear Science.* New York: Fawcett World Library, 1966.

———. *Physics and Beyond.* New York: Harper & Row, 1971.

———. *Physics and Philosophy.* New York: Harper & Row, 1958.

Herbert, Nick. *Quantum Reality.* Garden City, NY: Anchor Press, 1985.

Hilts, Philip J. *Scientific Temperaments.* New York: Simon & Schuster, 1982.

Hoffman, Banesh. With collaboration of Helen Dukas. *Albert Einstein, Creator and Rebel.* New York: Viking Press, 1972.

Hofstader, Douglas R. *Gödel, Escher, Bach.* New York: Basic Books, 1979.

———. and Dennett, Daniel C. *The Mind's I.* New York: Basic Books, 1981.

Holton, Gerald, *Thematic Origins of Scientific Thought.* Cambridge, MA: Harvard University Press, 1973.

Hoyle, Fred. *The Intelligent Universe.* New York: Holt, Rinehart & Winston, 1983.

——— and Wickramasinghe, Chandra. *Evolution from Space.* New York: Simon & Schuster, 1982.

Jacob, François. *The Logic of Life.* New York: Pantheon Books, 1973.

———. *The Possible and the Actual.* New York: Pantheon Books, 1982.

Jaki, Stanley, L. *Brain, Mind and Computers.* South Bend, IN: Gateway Editions, 1969.

Jantsch, Erich. *The Self-Organizing Universe,* New York: Pergamon Press, 1980.

Jastrow, Robert. *The Enchanted Loom*. New York: Simon & Schuster, 1981.

———. *God and the Astronomers*. New York: Warner Books, 1978.

———. *Red Giants and White Dwarfs*. New York: Warner Books, 1979.

Judson, Horace Freeland. *The Eighth Day of Creation*. New York: Simon & Schuster, 1979.

Kaufman, William, III. *Black Holes and Warped Spacetime*. New York: Bantam Books, 1980.

Kline, Morris. *Mathematics: The Loss of Certainty*. London: Oxford University Press, 1980.

Konner, Melvin. *The Tangled Wing*. New York: Holt, Rinehart & Winston, 1982.

Kuhn, Thomas S. *The Essential Tension*. Chicago: University of Chicago Press, 1977.

———. *The Structure of Scientific Revolutions*. Chicago: University of Chicago Press, 1970.

Leakey, Richard E. *The Making of Mankind*. New York: E. P. Dutton, 1981.

Londberg, David. *Science in the Middle Ages*. Chicago: University of Chicago Press, 1978.

Lovell, Bernard. *Emerging Technology*. New York: Columbia University Press, 1981.

Lovelock, J. E. *Gaia: A New Look at Life on Earth*. London: Oxford University Press, 1979.

Lumsden, Charles J., and Wilson, Edward O. *Genes, Mind, and Culture: The Coevolutionary Process*. Cambridge, MA: Harvard University Press, 1981.

Maffei, Paolo. *Beyond the Moon*. Translated by D.J.K. O'Connell. Cambridge, MA: MIT Press, 1978.

Mandelbrot, Benoit. *Fractals: Form, Chance, and Dimension*. San Francisco: W. H. Freeman, 1977.

Margulis, Lynn. *Early Life*. Boston: Science Books International, 1982.

———. *Symbiosis in Cell Evolution*. San Francisco: W. H. Freeman, 1981.

——— and Schwartz, Karlenz. *Five Kingdoms: An Illustrated Guide to the Phyla of Life on Earth*. San Francisco: W. H. Freeman, 1982.

Mayr, Ernst. *The Growth of Biological Thought*. Cambridge, MA: The

Belknap Press of Harvard University Press, 1982.

McLuhan, Marshall H. *Understanding Media.* New York: McGraw-Hill, 1964.

McCorduck, Pamela. *Machines Who Think.* San Francisco: W. H. Freeman, 1979.

McCormmach, Russell. *Night Thoughts of a Classical Physicist.* Cambridge, MA.: Harvard University Press, 1982.

Medawar, P. B., and Medawar, J. S. *The Life Science.* New York: Harper & Row, 1977.

Miller, George. *Language and Speech.* San Francisco: W. H. Freeman, 1981.

Morris, Richard. *Dismantling the Universe.* New York: Simon & Schuster, 1983.

————. *The End of the World.* Garden City, NY: Anchor Press, 1980.

————. *Evolution and Human Nature.* New York: Avon Books, 1983.

————. *The Fate of the Universe.* New York: Playboy Press, 1982.

————. *Time's Arrows.* New York: Simon & Schuster, 1985.

Narlikar, Jayant. *The Structure of the Universe.* London: Oxford University Press, 1977.

Nuttall, George H. F. *Blood Immunity and Blood Relationships.* New York: Macmillan, 1904.

O'Neill, Gerard. *The High Frontier.* New York: Bantam Books, 1979.

————. *2081.* New York: Simon & Schuster, 1981.

Pagels, Heinz R., editor. *Computer Culture.* New York: The New York Academy of Sciences, 1984.

Pagels, Heinz R. *The Cosmic Code.* New York: Simon & Schuster, 1982.

————. *Perfect Symmetry.* New York: Simon & Schuster, 1985.

Pais, Abraham. *"Subtle Is the Lord": The Science and Life of Albert Einstein.* London: Oxford University Press, 1982.

Pask, Gordon, and Curren, Susan. *Microman: Computers and the Evolution of Consciousness.* New York: Macmillan, 1982.

Peers, David. *Ludwig Wittgenstein.* New York: Viking Press, 1962.

Poundstone, William. *The Recursive Universe.* New York: William Morrow, 1985.

Portugal, Franklin H., and Cohen, Jack S. *A Century of DNA.* Cambridge, MA: MIT Press, 1977.

Prigogene, Ilya. *From Being to Becoming: Time and Complexity in the Physical Sciences.* San Francisco: W. H. Freeman, 1980.

Reichenbach, Hans. *The Rise of Scientific Philosophy*. Berkeley: University of California Press, 1968.

Rimbaud, Arthur. *A Season in Hell and The Drunken Boat*. Translated by Louise Varese. New York: New Directions, 1961.

Rowen-Robinson, Michael. *Cosmic Landscape: Voyages Back Along the Photon's Track*. London: Oxford University Press, 1979.

Rucker, Rudy. *Infinity and the Mind*. Boston: Birkhauser, 1982.

Sagan, Carl. *Broca's Brain*. New York: Random House, 1974.

————. *Cosmos*. New York: Random House, 1981.

————. *The Dragons of Eden*. New York: Random House, 1977.

Schilpp, Paul Arthur, editor. *Albert Einstein, Volume II*. New York: Harper & Row, 1949.

Schlossberg, Edwin. *Einstein and Beckett*. New York: Links Books, 1973.

Schneider, Stephen H., and Londer, Randi, *The Coevolution of Climate and Life*. San Francisco: Sierra Club Books, 1984.

Schrödinger, Erwin. *What Is Life? (and) Mind and Matter*. Cambridge, England: Cambridge University Press, 1967.

————. *Science Theory and Men*. New York: Dover Publications, 1957.

Segre, Emilio. *From X-Rays to Quarks*. San Francisco: W. H. Freeman, 1980.

Sheffield, Charles. *Earthwatch: A Survey of the World*. New York: Macmillan, 1981.

Sheldrake, Rupert. *A New Science of Life*. Los Angeles: J. P. Tarcher, 1981.

Shelley, Mary Wollstonecraft. *Frankenstein*. Chicago: University of Chicago Press, 1974.

Simpson, George. *The Meaning of Evolution*. New Haven, CT: Yale University Press, 1950.

Stanley, Steven M. *The New Evolutionary Timetable*. New York: Basic Books, 1982.

Stein, Gertrude. *Brewsie and Willie*. New York: Random House, 1946.

————. *The Gertrude Stein First Reader and Three Plays*. Dublin: Maurice Fridberg, 1946.

————. *Lectures in America*. Boston: Beacon Press, 1935.

————. *Narration*. Chicago: University of Chicago Press, 1969.

————. *The Selected Writings of Gertrude Stein*. New York: Random House, 1945.

————. *The Yale Gertrude Stein*. New Haven: Yale University Press, 1980.

Stent, Gunther. *The Coming of the Golden Age*. Garden City, NY: The Natural History Press, 1969.

Stevens, Wallace. *The Collected Poems of Wallace Stevens*. New York: Alfred A. Knopf, 1967.

————. *The Necessary Angel*. New York: Random House, 1951.

————. *Opus Posthumous*. New York: Alfred A. Knopf, 1966.

Sullivan, Walter. *Black Holes*. Garden City, NY: Anchor Press, 1979.

Tanner, Nancy. *On Becoming Human*. Cambridge, England: Cambridge University Press, 1981.

Tauber, Gerald, editor. *Albert Einstein's Theory of General Relativity*. New York: Crown Publishers, 1979.

Thom, René. *Structural Stability and Morphogenesis*. Reading, MA: Addison-Wesley, 1975.

Thomas, Lewis. *The Lives of a Cell*. New York: Viking Press, 1974.

————. *The Medusa and the Snail*. New York: Viking Press, 1979.

Thompson, D'Arcy, *On Growth and Form*. Cambridge, England: Cambridge University Press, 1942.

Trefil, James S. *The Moment of Creation*. New York: Charles Scribner's Sons, 1983.

Ulam, S. M. *Adventures of a Mathematician*. New York: Charles Scribner's Sons, 1976.

von Weizacker, Carl Frederich. *The Unity of Nature*. New York: Farrar Straus & Giroux, 1980.

Waddington, G. H. *Tools for Thought*. New York: Basic Books, 1977.

Walford, Roy L. *Maximum Life Span*. New York: W. W. Norton, 1983.

Watson, James D., and Tooze, John. *The DNA Story*. San Francisco: W. H. Freeman, 1981.

Watson, James D. *The Double Helix*. New York: Atheneum, 1968.

Weinberg, Steven. *The First Three Minutes*. New York: Basic Books, 1977.

Weisskopf, Victor W. *Knowledge and Wonder*. Cambridge, MA.: MIT Press, 1979.

Weizenbaum, Joseph. *Computer Power and Human Reason*. San Francisco: W. H. Freeman, 1976.

Wheeler, John; Misner, Charles; and Thorne, Kip. *Gravitation*. San Francisco: W. H. Freeman, 1973.

Whipple, Fred L. *Orbiting the Sun.* Cambridge, MA.: Harvard University Press, 1981.

White, Lynn, Jr. *Medieval Technology and Social Change.* London: Oxford University Press, 1962.

Wiener, Norbert. *Cybernetics.* Cambridge, MA: MIT Press, 1967.

————. *God & Golem, Inc.* Cambridge, MA: MIT Press, 1964.

————. *The Human Use of Human Beings: Cybernetics and Society.* New York: Avon Books, 1967.

————. *I Am a Mathematician.* Cambridge, MA.: MIT Press, 1956.

Wigner, Eugene. *Symmetries and Reflections.* Bloomington: Indiana University Press, 1967.

Wilson, Colin. *Starseekers.* Garden City, NY: Doubleday, 1980.

Wilson, Edward O. *On Human Nature.* Cambridge, MA.: Harvard University Press, 1978.

————. *Sociobiology: The New Synthesis.* Cambridge, MA.: Harvard University Press, 1975.

Winston, Patrick Henry. *Artificial Intelligence.* Reading, MA: Addison-Wesley, 1977.

Wittgenstein, Ludwig. *The Blue and Brown Books.* New York: Harper & Row, 1958.

————. *Philosophical Grammar.* Edited by Rush Rhees and translated by Anthony Kenny. Berkeley: University of California Press, 1974.

————. *Philosophical Investigations.* Translated by G.E.M. Anscombe. New York: Macmillan, 1958.

————. *Philosophical Remarks.* Edited by Rush Rhees and translated by Raymond Hargreaves and Roger White. Chicago: University of Chicago Press, 1975.

————. *Remarks on the Foundations of Mathematics.* Edited by G. H. von Wright, R. Rhees, and G.E.M. Anscombe, translated by G.E.M. Anscombe. Cambridge, MA.: MIT Press, 1967.

————. *Tractatus Logico-Philosophicus.* Translated by D. F. Pears and B. F. McGuiness. New York: The Humanities Press, 1960.

————. *Zettel.* Edited by G.E.M. Anscombe and G. H. von Wright. Translated by G.E.M. Anscombe. Berkeley: University of California Press, 1967.

Woolf, Harry, editor. *Some Strangeness in the Proportion.* Reading, MA: Addison-Wesley, 1980.

Grateful acknowledgment is made for permission to reprint the following previously published material:

Specified lines of poetry from "Doctrinal Point," in *Collected Poems of William Empson*, Copyright 1949, 1977 by William Empson. Reprinted by permission of Harcourt Brace Jovanovich, Inc.

Excerpts from "Adagia," in *Opus Posthumous*, by Wallace Stevens. Copyright 1975 by Wallace Stevens. Reprinted by permission of Alfred A. Knopf.

Specified lines of poetry from "Final Soliloquy of the Interior Paramour" and "Men Made Out of Words," in *The Collected Poems of Wallace Stevens*. Copyright 1967 by Wallace Stevens. Reprinted by permission of Alfred A. Knopf.